Notes
ON THE FLESH

by

Shahd Alshammari

First published in 2017 by
FARAXA
www.faraxapublishing.com
Email: info@faraxapublishing.com

Notes on the Flesh

ISBN 978-99957-48-67-8

Printed in the United States of America.

Disclaimer:
This is ultimately a work of fiction and a biomythography. Names, characters, businesses, places, events and incidents are either the products of the author's imagination or used in a fictitious manner. Any resemblance to actual persons, living or dead, or actual events is purely coincidental. The author depends on a failing memory, even when recording autobiographical events.

Prologue

I wrote this short story collection, part-memoir, part-illness narrative, part confused, part confusing, partially fabricated, partially the truth, and here it is. There are a mix of stories, of voices, but mainly, it is about women. Women who love, women who are too weak to love, women who marry for society, women who never forget their first love, women who are afraid of men, women who fight against men, women who leave their lovers, women who fight for education, and women who can't help but struggle to belong. These women tell their stories and sometimes the men tell theirs. Set in Kuwait, these are the unvoiced traumas, the repressed pleasures, and the tainted small, personal histories, of the very private acts of love. Every act, or lack thereof, is a small revolution. Love presents itself as a theme throughout, and the way it clashes with identity, society, and religion.

So here is a collection of moments, of reflections. The stories tend to flow in no order at all. There are moments when I am your unreliable narrator. There are moments when I recall the events as they happened, and yet there are times where I have tried to fill the gaps and inconsistencies. My memory fails me, as my body has failed me, and this is but an attempt at reconstructing the experience of love, loss, meaning, and purpose. These moments are sometimes nonfictional, sometimes made-up and unreal, and at others they are part of a *biomythography*, as Audre Lorde labels it. Lorde argued that biomythography tells the story, and sometimes stories, of the individual, weaving together different genres and realities. Fiction, nonfiction, poetry, history, they are all part of the narrative. *Notes on the Flesh* is written on the body, from the body, from existence, from the experience of being here, fully here, and sometimes, only there in my head, or through someone else's story, living vicariously through someone. Some of these stories are narrated by others, and as always, there is no boundary between the self and other. I am the Other, and the Other is me. I am the real character and the imagined. I am the unreliable narrator and the author. I am the one transferring the feeling and thought to you, but I have been drowning in existence, too.

At times, these stories are from the point of view of the villain, sometimes from the victim's unbearable narration, and like everything in life, it is hard to pinpoint a protagonist, a villain, and a victim. There are shorter glimpses into the inner consciousness of the characters. As with all works of literature, there is always a dialogue, always influence, always a re-creation, a re-writing, a re-assertion of voice.

Table of Contents

PART ONE

Mythography

Mama

She was not just a mother. Perhaps she was never meant for motherhood. But she managed to succeed, against all odds, and she was able to get her hands dirty – the muddy business of being a Palestinian mother in a strictly Bedouin culture. She had married him, my father, and he had been her choice. At only twenty, they had decided that they were in love. But they were not merely opposites. She was a Palestinian woman, a liberal, a woman who loved and enjoyed freedom, her short blonde hair always bouncing proudly, her clothes were always colorful: reds, blues, pinks. She despised black, yet years later was clothed in a black *abbaya* that his culture and traditions upheld as the norm.

To be able to fully understand my father's Bedouin background, I must first define the term Bedouin. Bedouin usually means nomad, and namely, the people of the Arabian Peninsula, the desert. Bedouins consist of different tribes. There are Bedouins all over the Gulf, but mainly, Saudi Arabia has the biggest population. My father's tribe originated from Saudi Arabia. None of his family are educated. Most women are married off at a very early age, expected to give birth to boys, rather than girls, for the tribe only celebrated the birth of boys.

My mother married my father because she fell in love with him. She fell in love with the exotic image of the Bedouin man, with his love for horses, camels, oral poetry, and his noble characteristics. Because she married him, she lost everybody who loved her. Her family nearly disowned her, and his family cursed him for tainting the blood of the tribe. She was an outsider to them, a stranger – and she remained a stranger. She wasn't veiled when she first married him. She loved short skirts, and yet his jealousy and his tribal upbringing drove him mad. Once she was pregnant, she wanted to get rid of the child; that child was me. She felt suffocated by the child's impending existence, and couldn't bring herself to imagine being a mother to a child that would be fathered by a strict Bedouin man. She was terrified both for herself and the child. She hoped it would be a boy, only so that he could detach from him. A boy would be able to take care of himself. A boy would have rights. A boy would be defended, a girl would be attacked for life. Abortion was not possible, and yet she tried every way she could think of. She was a twenty-year-old who was not ready to have a child, and had realized that she had made a grave mistake marrying this man.

The child persisted, and wouldn't go. The child was born: a healthy girl to two completely different parents. Her father looked at his newborn and wished it was a boy, he was tired of having girls. He had been married before, married to his cousin, and he had five girls. I was my father's sixth daughter, and my mother's only child.

By the time I was two or three years old, she had developed a fear of losing me. My paternal grandmother, a strong and cruel tribal woman, threatened my mother constantly. She threatened her that I would be kidnapped, that I would be sent away to some place in Iraq, where no one could find me. She wanted to teach my mother a lesson, she said.

"A lesson of loss. So you know what it's like to have your child taken away from you. The same way you took my son." Those were my grandmother's words. These words haunted my mother forever. She didn't know if she would be able to keep me, if she would be able to find me if I was taken away. She taught me, by the time I could speak, the word "Embassy." She instructed me carefully, teaching me that it was important to find my way home.

"Always find me, *Mama*. First, find the embassy. The embassy will find your Mama," she said.

But I didn't get taken away from her. Instead, I grew up in fear and hatred. I grew up knowing that my mother and I were outsiders, hated by everyone. My half-sisters hated me and bullied me, made fun of my mother, her origins, and my inability to speak proper Arabic. My mother had insisted on a Western education for me because she was afraid I would never have what it takes to build character. She didn't want me to feel connected to my father's culture, nor hers. She didn't want a middle ground for me. She wanted me to find myself outside their circle. And I did. I never could understand the concept of belonging, of fitting in. We despised squares, Mama and I.

She would draw a circle for me and show me how the circle had infinite possibilities. Endless. Limitless. There was no way out of the circle, but to keep going. To fight, to persevere. It depends how you viewed the circle. Was the circle as oppressive as a square? As hierarchical as a triangle? The circle was movement, endless movement, and we had no alternative, but to keep moving, in a world that tried to stop women from moving.

That is how the concept of family shifted to only mean Mama. Mama was my family. And Mama was the woman who bargained for my freedom. She would pay for my education, he wouldn't have to worry about the finances. She worked double shifts to do that, and there were many days where she couldn't afford to buy my basic needs: clothes, food, school supplies. Yet Mama managed. She did it, all on her own. She says she is like the candle that burns for me, gives my path light, and like all candles, it's what she does best. She didn't want me to begin with, and I came into this world unwanted.

I have found that these stories of how you come into the world, what you do in your initial years of life, these are the stories that build your climax, your story, and grant you purpose.

Notes on the Flesh

Early Years

Like most kids, when I first started speaking as a toddler, I could say Mama and Baba; but I was confused as to who was who. Mama was also Baba, and Baba was also Mama. I couldn't tell the difference. A bit after that confusion was rectified, I started experimenting with language. Words were very important, and I quickly realized that Mama spoke a different dialect than Baba. Because I loved them both equally, I ended up mixing dialects, both Palestinian and Kuwaiti, and created my own dialect. Nobody seemed to mind. It was accepted and I remained comfortable with this until I was exposed to school, and people outside of our tiny circle of safety and love.

I was first enrolled in a Public school, an Arabic speaking school. My father wanted me to speak fluent Kuwaiti, and I could only grow accustomed to a strict and conservative culture if I was placed in a school that mirrored our culture's traditions and habits. He was very comfortable with this decision, while my mother wasn't. It so happened that when I entered first grade in elementary school, it was a few months after the Gulf War in 1990. Iraq, Kuwait's neighboring country, had invaded Kuwait. I remember the trauma of living through the war, although not vividly. I was only five years old, and my recollection of the memory is vague.

I remember that I had a black bike, a three-wheel that Baba bought me. The beautiful bike was black, not pink, and not blue, not a flashy color, and I must have felt very grown-up owning it. The bike was always parked in the middle of the living room, and I took pride in its uniqueness. No other kid in our neighborhood had a black bike, until the night that a group of Iraqi soldiers kicked our apartment door open, and demanded to know where my father was.

My father was a Public Prosecutor at the time, and anybody who worked with the police or Kuwaiti government was taken hostage and held as Prisoner of War. Iraqi soldiers were always on the lookout for men who could be a threat to the Sadam regime, anyone who was against the invasion, and people who were considered too loyal to Kuwait. Someone had ratted my father out, given his home address to the Iraqi army. My mother informed them that we hadn't seen him in months, and for some bizarre reason, they left it at that. She swears that the only reason we remained safe that night was because she read verses from the Quran under her breath begging Allah for support, strength, and for him to "shield the enemy's eyes from what they are looking for." Thankfully, the only things they ended up taking that night were the television, a few tables, the fridge in the kitchen, canned food which my mother had stocked up on, and my black bike.

We fled the country a few days after this incident, and my father drove us across the Kuwaiti-Saudi Arabia borders, until we reached Hail, a city in Saudi Arabia. My father had extended family there, people he had never met, people who belonged to the same tribe. We spent months sleeping on the floor in a tiny room, covered in one wool blanket, a brown one, one that Mama says was enough for us. Baba left my mother and me a few times during the war, as he was looking for his brother, my uncle, who was taken as a POW. He was a policeman too, and he had been captured back in Kuwait, taken to some unknown Iraqi police station in Basra, Iraq. My father risked his life trying to find him, and he followed every lead that he got, every piece of news. He gathered money from most of the members of the tribe, just so that he could buy his brother's freedom back. Every time he met with an Iraqi soldier, he would beg to see his brother, to be lead to where he was taken, and he swore he would pay whatever price was asked of him. He would have sold an organ if he had to, and he was left completely deluded, told that his brother was alive and well, taken to an official prison, and that he would be released in due time. His brother was never released, and Baba never saw his brother again.

Fast forward to the day of Kuwait's liberation, Feb 26, 1991. After the help of the US government, President George Bush (who became a national heroic figure to all Kuwaitis), Kuwait was finally free. Iraqi troops left Kuwait, but not after a massacre had taken place, and the burning of oil wells was left as a reminder of everything that was lost. My parents drove back home on the morning of February 28, and yet, all we saw was black skies. We couldn't tell it was morning, until we were met with a Kuwaiti soldier near the border who welcomed us back home, said good morning to us, and gave us a brand-new Quran as a gift, a blessing.

What happened after the invasion was a collection of events that cannot be relayed in stories and words.

What happened was that an entire nation was shocked, a nation was traumatized, and there were those who were never the same again. My parents were part of the group of people who felt betrayed by the world, who were undeniably grateful to the US army, and who couldn't fathom the cruelty of the war. Because many Arab states were divided in terms of who they supported during the war (Iraq or Kuwait), we were affected at home. Jordan and Palestine were countries that supported the Iraqi Invasion of Kuwait. As a result, thousands of Palestinians were expelled from Kuwait. Others had fled during the war, going to other countries they now had to call home.

My mother's family was gone. Not one person remained. And so it was, that Mama lost her family, her identity, and her sense of belonging. From then on I was no longer allowed to speak Palestinian and had to speak Kuwaiti. Mama started speaking Kuwaiti, to protect me from bullying that took place in the streets and at school. Even my father's family made fun of me. I started stuttering in public, because speech was no longer safe. Every time I mixed my parents' dialects, I was told off by one of them. Slowly, language was used as a weapon. All around me was hate. If I mispronounced a Kuwaiti word, I was glared at, criticized, and once people found out my mother was Palestinian, she became the real culprit. She was being punished for a crime she hadn't committed. It was hard enough that she lost her family, here she was, trying to make sense of a new identity, embrace a new dialect, and help me find a balance between her culture and my father's. Sometimes I wonder how she was able to do it. Is it motherly love that gave her the strength to pull through in the face of war? Was it the strong Palestinian woman's genes? What I do know is that she managed to create a small, personal revolution. Within me, she instilled a love for freedom, independence, of speaking up, and of not being afraid to say yes. I am a woman, a tribal woman, a hybrid, a disabled woman, but so what? She taught me to say "So what?" in the face of society's discrimination and cruelty.

When I cried to her about Kuwaiti teachers making fun of me at school in the first grade, she sat me down, and explained politics to me. In a very simple way, she said, "There are good and bad people in the world. Good people will not make fun of you if you are different, if your mother is different, if you speak differently. Bad people will be mean to you if you are not like them. Do you want to be like these bad people?"

"No," I answered firmly.

"Good. Now let us find you a different school," she replied, almost speaking to herself.

That is how I ended up enrolled in a private American school. She wanted me to feel like I didn't have to belong to my father's background or hers. Mama wanted me to mix cultures, traditions, languages, English and Arabic, views, ideologies, and end up enmeshed within multiple identities.

High School

I have always thought high school was best represented in Mean Girls. Yet it was difficult to relate to that, because our high school was an American high school, located in the Arab world, somewhere in the Middle East. Hallways were infested with hormonal teenagers, boys who shaved unnecessarily, and girls who waxed their upper lip, ashamed of the tiny black hairs that shone in the sun. The general consensus was that co-ed schools familiarized us with the opposite sex. You were in the presence of boys, and as such, did not feel deprived of testosterone, unlike girls who attended public schools –we thought they were insanely hormonal, always on the look-out for boys. This was a perfect deal for private school boys. All they had to do was scout for public school girls, who would worship them immediately.

Of course, the same could not be said of private school girls. We were cooler. Private school girls, whether veiled or not, were considered superior. They were always, always, hard to get. Since mixed high schools blended Westernization with our own Islamic background and Arab traditional culture, it was always chaotic, to say the least. Finding a balance between one's raging hormones, sexual tension, and the piety we were supposed to maintain was a constant battle. Would you allow a boy to hold your hand? Kiss you, perhaps? You could never tell anyone (except your friends, who could out you) in case it gets to your brother. No decent brother would consent to his sister fornicating with men (boys, really). But of course, the brother, the King of all, *the Shaikh* of all, could do whatever and whomever. Men had an Untouchable air to them.

A typical school day, much like any institution, is made up of plain school uniforms, lunch time, and lots of screeching bells. American teachers would keep the hallways secured, screaming "Oi!" if anything was deemed slightly out of order.

I strolled across the hallway, surrounded by my group of friends. We had arranged our schedules in a way so that we could take most of our core classes together. Luckily for us, we had that type of flexibility. After all, it was an American school. American schools, unlike British schools, were synonymous with "easygoing."

My friends did not belong to the "coolest" clique; they were considered the hybrids, neither fully here, nor there. Most of our mothers were not *Khaleejis*[1] which immediately marginalized us. The group consisted of three girls, two guys, and myself.

"I am so happy I'm back home Sarah," a high-pitched voice said. I looked at Salma and smiled at her declaration.

"Me too. It's our senior year," I replied. Salma's father, a strict, Shiite conservative, had married an American. Her mother, Jane, was a beautiful woman, and I liked to think of her as a martyr. She had raised nine children, embraced Islam, and continued to

---

[1]   Originating from Gulf countries

Notes on the Flesh

struggle with maintaining the family's closeness. Her children had to be fully Arab, yet they were not. Salma's father, Ali, was a gruff-looking man, who only smiled if he approved of you. He had approved of me, labeling me as a "good girl" and supported Salma's friendship with me. He hoped she would learn a thing or two from me about our so-called "conservative" Arab culture. Salma had recounted to me the details of her father's conversation with her in between bouts of laughter.

"So luckily for us Sarah, he doesn't think you'll guide me to the wrong path! If only he knew we both had crushes on two of the hottest guys ever!" Salma had laughed at her father's misconceptions.

Because Salma was a hybrid, she truly had the best of both worlds. Her beauty was touched by both East and West, a perfect mixture of the two. Her blue eyes were her mother's, while her black hair was her father's. Her thick Persian eyebrows were inquisitive and always groomed. At the age of thirteen, her father had forced her to wear the veil. There was no way around it, and Salma had obliged. I remember the day she cried her heart out before she showed up to school, wearing the *hijab*. After that day, she was treated differently. Boys no longer approached her as easily, and way too often, other girls judged her harshly. They assumed she was "too religious" and, by extension, plain boring. A piece of clothing immediately made her uncool.

Salma was anything but boring. In fact, she was truly a knitted ball of contradictions. There were times where she did not make sense at all, not even to herself. She was hardly silent, she always had something to say, something to inquire about.

I had met Salma when I was fifteen years old, but being the socially-awkward person that I am, I had never been able to be friends with anyone. At home, there was always something going on with the family. My closest friend was my mother, and I could never admit that to anyone. What teenager actually likes, let alone adores their mother? Again, I was weird. Salma was able to see through my weirdness and actually enjoy my company. Because my mother was also a foreigner, somehow, I could connect to Salma on a deeper level. We bonded and depended on each other for advice and support, and revealed things to each other that were considered 'taboo' by everyone else. In our culture, you're not supposed to talk about things. You can gossip, you can talk about people, you can talk about the latest fashion trends – but don't talk about the family. Family, is always sacred. The private sphere, in general, is very protected, and that is where all the trouble starts.

Salma and I would hang out together all the time at school, and I would go over to her place after school. We would talk about guys. A fun topic for teenagers. But I struggled to find someone to invest all my energies in, someone that my conversations would revolve around.

And that's when I met him. He was my friend Amina's brother. Once, I went over to her house for a movie night, and he opened the door for me. He literally and figuratively opened *the door* for me. I saw Hassan as the beam of sunlight I so desperately needed. He was the epitome of handsome: tall, dark, thin, not built, and most importantly, he wore eyeglasses. He flashed beautiful white teeth at me, and his eyes had a certain gentleness in them that I immediately yearned for. He told me that that I had a beautiful smile, and I held on to that compliment like there was no tomorrow. Braces had definitely come in handy. This was the first nice thing a guy had said to me.

Now the truth of the matter is, we didn't really date. Dating in the West is obviously not synonymous to dating in the East. And not to mention that this was the time where NSYNC and Backstreet Boys were still hip, where we only had text message communication, no Facebook, no social media of any sort. But it was easier to keep track of things, and messages had a sentimental value, perhaps in the same way that hand-written letters trumped emails. I would re-read his messages all night long, taking in his words, and feeling as though I finally stood a chance at being like everyone else. It helped that Hassan was kind, gentle, funny, and craved my friendship. Our "dating" was actually friendship with a hint of courting techniques. He gave me butterflies in my stomach and all that ordeal. I rushed to meet him after school, for five or ten minutes, where we would shake hands, and let our fingers linger in that touch.

"He's a bad boy. That's why you're attracted to him. Do you know he smokes? Actually, uses drugs?" Salma asked me.

"He's not. He's a poet, he's sensitive, and he doesn't do drugs!" I defended him, always.

Rumor had it that Hassan was a troubled soul, someone who was angry at the world, and was not to be trusted. But I saw him as a good man, a most loyal companion, and could not fathom why anybody would view him in that awful light. I learned a lot about love and life from him (theoretically of course, and Hollywood depictions of it), and enjoyed talking to him all night long about books and movies, dreams and hopes, faith and disbelief. Finally, after spending what seemed to be an eternity in High School, Hassan had arrived, making it all seem worthwhile.

Then there was the pressing problem of Salma in my life. She needed me constantly, and I the same. But her life demanded my attention. She struggled with family and her tyrannical brothers. We tried to get away with things, without them ever noticing. Salma had five brothers, all who looked American, light blonde hair, blue eyes and yet they adopted a very patriarchal mindset-in the name of Islam of course. It frustrated both of us, so we had to devise plans of sneaking her out of the house, finding a certain routine that would enable us to leave the house unnoticed, and go to malls during times of the day where we were sure not to run into anyone.

One day, I decided to be a great friend and find Salma a boyfriend who would make her feel smart and beautiful, someone who would say all the right things, and make all the right moves. I chose wisely and carefully. I chose one of my closest guy friends, Ahmad. Ahmad happened to be related to Hassan.

"What do you say to that? He's stunning, and a good guy. He won't cause any trouble and I'm sure he doesn't know your brothers," I told her.

Salma hesitated at first, but soon enough, she was sold on the idea. She told me that she was now afraid every night. Her brother entered the housemaid's room late at night, but nobody wanted to acknowledge it.

"Are you sure? How do you know?" I asked, dumbfounded.

"Yes, Sarah, and the worst part is, nobody believes her. My mom can't bring herself to imagine that her angel could harm anyone. Let alone a Filipino maid!

Can you believe she actually said, that there's no way he would be attracted to her! As if that was the real problem!"

"I don't know."

Salma looked at me, searching for any kind of reaction. I must have had one of my completely blank looks. I wasn't pretending. I really didn't know. Her brother was immaculately polished, smart, and charismatic. You'd never think. Up until that moment, I thought all abusers looked the same, unshaved beards, dark, smelly, poor, everything we didn't associate ourselves with. I thought they belonged to a different social class.

"I understand you're just being polite. But he's an idiot!" Salma said, her eyes fuming with anger.

I looked at her for a while before deciding what to say. She never struck me as the empathetic type, and she was getting very worked up. Plus, she had said she was afraid…

"Are you afraid that Shanti might report him to her embassy?"

"I wish she would –I know he's my brother, but it's getting scary. I have to lock my door at night and still he comes knocking on the door around two am; I keep saying 'Go away' over and over again. I just hate how I can't tell my mom. I know she'll call me a liar, just like she screamed at Shanti and threatened to send her away," Salma said without so much as glancing at me. It's peculiar how it's easiest to say things without looking at your audience. There's a semi-sense of detachment. It gives you the illusion that your listener isn't really listening, isn't really able to see right through you.

I was horrified at her confession and was unable to say anything for a few minutes. What could I have said?

"Keep locking your door," I finally managed to say. I nodded my head as though I was reaffirming my own words.

"I will," she said.

And that was the last time we ever spoke about it.

Stroke of Evil

Nearly five months after Salma and Ahmad started dating, as I was getting closer to Hassan, we finally decided that it was time that we all go out together as a group. Call it double dating if you like. But really, it was for practical purposes. We felt that it was time for us to actually go out with the guys, because usually, we weren't able to see them. Salma specifically was unable to leave the house, except for school. That was the only time she actually interacted with people who weren't family. Even at school, her brothers would keep an eye on her, since they also went to our school. When it was Ahmad's birthday, she was unable to buy him a gift. So she gave me enough money and I went shopping for a gift for her boyfriend. I even picked the birthday card, wrapped the gift in manly wrapping paper, and headed to her house triumphantly to show her that I had accomplished the mission. After all, I wanted to be the person closest to her. She trusted me, and I trusted her. There was no doubt about that at this point.

She hugged me tightly, thanking me for being so wonderful. I lingered.

"I'm so excited about going out with Ahmad and you and Hassan! You know, sometimes I can't help but imagine what our lives would be like if we both married them! They're best friends, and we're best friends, and it'll just be…perfect!" Salma beamed at me.

I shuffled my feet and found myself unable to reiterate that same wish. Instead, I just said that I thought it was time for me to stop wearing eyeglasses. I had been wearing eyeglasses ever since I could remember, and I had only recently stopped wearing braces. My teeth were fine at this point, after years of agonizing bullying and social awkwardness. I felt as though the eyeglasses were the real problem now. Maybe, if people could see my eyes, if people could see past the ugly eyeglasses (at the time I really believed they were hideous), then I would attract more boys.

"I think that'd be great. You can even get colored lenses if you like…maybe grey? They might look nice with your complexion," Salma affirmed.

"No, no! That's too much. Not me at all. I don't know how I'll be poking my eye, let alone look like a fool."

She let it go and I was relieved. I never talked about physical looks. It was a topic that made me very uncomfortable.

After a few weeks of waking up two hours before school just to pop in those plastic things that felt glued to my eyes, I finally got the hang of it. Amazingly, it made me feel more confident than usual. The first thing I did was buy several pairs of sunglasses. Granted, they were all the same color, but they were different brands and I was still trying to be cool. Little did I know that I would never get there.

We arranged for an outing together, we chose a Starbucks that was close to home. The Middle East is filled with McDonalds and Starbucks. It's a little insane to think that it has become a mirror to the west, to America in particular. Like a Beverly Hills television series, we planned to go out with the guys, and so we did. The coffee date was awkward at first but soon became your typical two guys and two girls outing: the guys would crack jokes, and us girls would laugh. The guys' egos inflated (and I suspect a little something in their jeans), and it was recorded as a successful double date. Afterwards, we decided to go cruising in the car. At the time, neither Salma nor I were eighteen, but the boys were, and so Hassan drove while I sat in the passenger's seat. Before we knew it, I noticed that he was shifting in his seat uncomfortably. Then he raised the volume –a song by Backstreet Boys was playing and of course he despised boy bands. I realized that Salma and Ahmad were kissing in the backseat. That was the first time I was unable to explain my feelings to myself. I felt nauseous and afraid. I was afraid for her, but also afraid to be in a car with guys. Police could stop the car any second, and once they discover that we aren't married or related, they could easily drag us to the Police Station where our guardians would be called in to 'collect' us. My face went red, mirroring Hassan's furious face. He was not happy.

By the time we arrived home, Salma was ecstatic. She felt that everything finally made sense, that this was the man of her dreams.

"Sarah, you have no idea. His breath on me. He tasted like coffee and cigarettes, but more than that. There was something tangy in his breath. Maybe mint. He could have had one before kissing me…which means he was planning to!" Salma squealed with delight.

"I guess. Wow. You liked it?"

"It was so good! I'd do it over and over again if I could! Wait, let me message him. Or should I wait? Maybe I should wait."

"Well maybe you should wait. Let him message you. I bet he's really happy. It's a big deal you know. You actually kissed. He knows you wouldn't do this with any other guy," I responded.

"It's because I trust him. And I know I'll marry him. His family is great, and my father wouldn't object at all."

I listened carefully to her words, trying to gauge meaning from the meaninglessness of the situation. I didn't know what it was like to kiss someone. I didn't understand how she wanted to marry Ahmad. Just like that. But I had been the one to set them up, and my choice had been wise. They were both Shiites and the union would be blessed by both families. Or so we thought. Soon, Ahmad did message.

It took him two hours to come up with one line: "It's over."

Salma didn't understand what was over, what he meant, and most importantly, why? What was he talking about? When she asked, he wouldn't respond. He left her hanging, confused, and stricken with grief. I tried to speak to him but he asked me to stay out of it. Finally, I managed to get a clearer answer from Hassan.

"Look babe, I shouldn't be the one to say this. But you know how it is. She's not as pure as he thought she would be. I mean come on, for God's sake, she's veiled! How could she make out with him?! Do you blame him for breaking up with her?" Hassan asked me, aggressively.

Silence.

There was nothing to say. I was beyond disappointed. In Hassan, in Ahmad, in Arab men, in Salma, and in myself. Nothing felt right anymore. What

Notes on the Flesh

had her mistake been? The fact that she had kissed her boyfriend? Hassan made her sound like a prostitute, and Ahmad was horrible for misinterpreting my best friend's actions. It was simply unfair. And I had to deliver the message to her, in my own way, without hurting her feelings. Like that was possible.

I told her that he was a confused guy, that he didn't know what he wanted from life. I told her that she deserved better. I told her everything that girlfriends say when they're consoling each other.

She looked right at me, and said the words I was dreading, "Sarah, it's all because I kissed him. I'm worthless now."

"It's not that, I'm sure. Maybe the kiss wasn't good. Maybe he's gay."

"What? No of course it was good! And he's not gay! How can you even think that?"

"I'm just saying. You never know."

"No, I know. I know him. There's no such thing. You know if the person you're dating is gay. You're that close! Let's just not talk about it. I'm over it."

We let it go. But I knew she still thought of him. And I knew that he had broken something in her. Her pride was shattered. I wasn't able to comfort her, and my instincts to take care of her heightened. Over time, she stopped returning my calls. At school, she started befriending others. She chose to hang out with two other friends, girls she had not considered worthy of her time before. I wasn't someone she wanted to be around. That much was clear.

I got my driving license the day of my birthday. I woke up early in the morning and my father had bought me a beautiful, second-hand car. It was so sleek and smooth. I drove it to school, and received so many compliments.

Everyone swooned over the car. I remember that it was at that moment where it really hit me: everyone was just so materialistic. A car managed to change the way everyone treated me. I was no longer invisible.

I decided to go over to Salma's house. I sent her a message before doing so, and she agreed, saying that she had to give me my birthday gift anyway. At this point, things were shaky between us and I was still unsure why. When I arrived at her place, she would not take me to her room. Instead, we remained in the living room, where we could hear the television blasting incoherent religious sermons, and we could smell the stench of whatever was cooking in the kitchen. Onions, mixed with garlic. The scent was not as disturbing as what was about to happen. She handed me my gift, which turned out to be a Teddy Bear. He was dressed in a black suit, red tie, and was wearing sunglasses. I pretended to love it.

I hugged her, and she stiffened. I could feel every muscle in her back contract as she released herself from my arms. She sat back down on her chair and started rocking back and forth. In a burst of emotional vulnerability, I put my hands on the chair and stopped her. I sat down on the floor, placing my hands on the chair so that she would not be able to move. I looked at her and asked her what was going on.

"Why are you acting so distant? Are you mad at me? I don't understand," I said pleadingly. I was completely confused.

She remained quiet for a few minutes and then finally said the words that had scarred me for a very long time: "Sarah, you are evil."

"What?"

"Some people pretend to be good, and kind. But inside of you, there's a lot of evil. Evil is in you. I see it in your eyes. I see it in the way you look at me," Salma said, and added, "and the way you talk to me. It's just repulsive."

I stood up from my position, with tears in my eyes, of course. I didn't understand how she had given me a birthday gift, if she thought I was 'evil.' She seemed very serious about my evil nature. I felt as though I had been hit by a bus. I felt paralyzed. I took my gift and headed for the door. I went home and cried to my mother like a child.

"Don't cry. I didn't raise you to cry. You're being weak," my ever-so strong, ever so lovely mother said.

"But Mama I don't understand what I did wrong? I was a good friend and I loved her so much. Why does she hate me?" I looked at my mother, knowing she had all the answers in the world. At the time, I really believed my mother knew everything there was to know in the world. She had to have an explanation for all of this.

"You need to learn to stop loving people too much. Let go."

"Without knowing why? I can't do that!"

"With time, everything unfolds, everything heals. Give it time. Give it space. Just leave her alone Sarah," my mother told me.

And so I did. For a few days. Once I arrived at school on Sunday morning, everyone was furious with me. I headed to the lunch table where we would usually sit as a group, and found that everyone left the table. Nobody wanted to speak to me, let alone sit at the same table with me. This was the table we used to sit at for years. I was suddenly the biggest social outcast. I had no idea who to talk to, who would explain to me what was going on, and if anyone would actually answer me, -so I asked one of our mutual friends, Faten.

Faten sighed before she explained the problem to me. She said that she was very disappointed in me, because she had thought that I was a genuinely good person. How could I have been so horrible? Why did I tell Salma's brothers that Salma had a boyfriend? Did I have any idea the kind of agony she had to go through?

"That's why she had a blue eye the other day at school. You didn't notice, did you?" Faten asked me, looking at me with murder in her eyes.

"What?! Of course I didn't tell her brothers anything! Are you out of your mind?"

"I'm just saying. You know you did it. Just own up to it and apologize. Although really, if you ask me, I don't see why she would forgive you. You've really betrayed her," Faten said. Then she walked away without looking back.

I stood dumbfounded in the girls' locker room. I just stood there. I was being accused of something I hadn't done. I had never felt what it was like to be wrongfully accused before. I gave myself a few minutes before I ran out to confront Salma. Once I did, she refused to look at me. Her tone was ice cold. Her features had darkened and her eyes were hollow. She asked me never to speak to her again, and it was bad enough that I was "too naïve." I asked what she meant, and she responded with the simple answer, that answer that is all too-ready, the two words that slit your throat: "You know." And I had no idea.

The next three months at school were hellish. Torture at its worst. I was bullied every time I entered a class, for ratting out my best friend. Nobody would talk to me or sit next to me in class. Each time, I felt my face go on fire. Heat arose in my body, and I was clothed in shame. I could barely speak in class. She would sit next to our mutual friends, socialize with them, laugh at the world's silliest jokes, and I would just want to die. Anger is a nasty feeling, especially when it's mixed with confusion and pain. I was angry because I was wrongfully accused. I was angry because nobody would listen to me, let alone believe me. There was no point in talking because my words meant nothing to anyone.

One day, I woke up unable to see anything – one eye was completely blurred. Doctors didn't know what was wrong. They couldn't figure it out, and all they suggested was to wear one of those eye patches. Keep it shut, they said. It'll clear up on its own. One doctor suspected it could be neurological in origin, but could not prove it without an MRI. My father refused to pay for an MRI and brushed it off as just 'stress.' So I went to school for nearly a month with an eye patch. And that's how I got the nickname "Blind Girl." It was humiliating and I took it silently. I thought it would stop at some point, go away on its own, that they would stop calling me that. I remember the first time a classmate called me Blind Girl, I gasped. I was astonished. It was Lesson 101 in Human Cruelty. I was officially 'Blind Girl.' I think it's written somewhere in the Senior Yearbook.

I spent the last few weeks of school writing letters. Handwritten letters. And e-mails. Lots of those too. Of course, they were always addressed to Salma. They were agonizingly long, and Lame. Lame with a Capital L. Looking back, I can safely say that they were the letters and e-mails of a heartbroken eighteen-year-old girl. Disappointed with life, or what I knew of life. I begged. I pleaded. I said I missed her. I said I cared about her. I even said that I would try and find out who told her brothers that she was dating. All my attempts went unanswered. She didn't want to acknowledge my confessions. My apologies. I didn't know what exactly

I was apologizing for. I didn't know whether that was what was expected of me. But I did it anyway.

Now these letters were ten-page letters, minimum. My hand hurt. My eyes hurt. It wasn't easy. But I persisted, hoping that somehow, everything would be sorted out. I would leave them in her locker, and wait for a reply. At the time, I had no one. Even Hassan was no longer there. When he found out I was having problems with my vision, he wasn't able to deal with it. He claimed he was busy with his classes, busy studying, and I should just "take good care of myself." I wasn't disappointed with his response. I didn't have enough disappointment reserved for him. My heart ached from too many losses.

I found myself at her house one day. I parked the car and just waited. I called her phone, she would not reply -surprise, surprise. I honked. And honked. I wanted to raise hell. She needed to see me. The noise I caused must have generated necessary attention because her younger sister, Mariam, came outside to see me. She asked me to come in, which I did. There was no need for an invitation. You'd think that Salma would speak to me once I was in her home. But she looked at me as though I was a stranger, picked up her phone, dialed a number, and started talking to a friend. While I just stared and waved my hand at her, she walked away. In circles. Around me. Perhaps it was a strategic way of keeping me in place, after all, I couldn't exactly follow her in circles too.

I gave up. I drove home that night, barely able to see in the dark, and felt utterly alone.

Graduation

Graduation was approaching. I could hardly wait to leave school, leave the horrible memories behind. When graduation day finally arrived, I was lucky enough to have regained my eyesight. I removed the patch, wore my contacts, and prepared for the day ahead. It was the last day of classes and we all got a chance to say goodbye to each other, although we were seeing each other at the graduation ceremony a week after. We had cake passed out to all the seniors and everyone rejoiced in their supposed success, people signed each other's yearbooks, gave each other their contact details for the 'future' and made sure to tell each other how much they would miss these times shared, in this school, for the past twelve years of our lives. Many tears were shed. In my case, I had none of the above. Nobody signed my yearbook, nobody took pictures with me, and I doubt anyone wanted to stay in touch with me. While the girls hugged each other, I merely stood aside, searching the crowds for anyone with a slightly familiar face, anybody who would seem approachable at that moment.

Salma patted me on the shoulder. I turned around and said, "Hey," and stuck my hand out tentatively. My hand must have instilled a shocking sensation in her, before even touching hers. She gawked in astonishment at my hand – it was as though I had unknowingly insulted her. But she shook it anyway. Politeness. Always so necessary. Boiling underneath the simmering pot of politeness was a hatred we both knew existed between us, a rift that would not heal.

"Congratulations," Salma managed to say, between gritted teeth.

"Congratulations," I mumbled.

We both left it at that. Like a timed move in a choreographed dance, we turned around, and walked away from each other. *Exit Stage.*

Between repressed tears and a horrible knot in my stomach, I was barely emotionally functional. Graduation night was horrible in every sense of the word. At first, I refused to go. But my father, being the wonderful man that he is, insisted that I ought to face the storm. That I should be stronger, that I should face whatever I am most afraid of.

"Never show the enemy weakness. That is when he attacks. You must always pretend to be brave, in the hope that you may fool your opponent," he said, nodding his head at his own words.

I took the advice.

Graduation was very much a group event. It required interaction with others. You couldn't be the outcast and expect to suddenly be included in the celebration. That night, I felt like a beggar, begging for attention from any of my 'friends' and classmates. I wanted to at least take pictures with people, so that I may somehow fool myself into remembering the night fondly. I've actually hidden the photos in the bottom drawer of my desk, never to be framed, hung on walls, or any of that stuff.

Its years later and the photos really bring about feelings of shame and humiliation, but I can't bring myself to throw them out. High school graduation is supposedly a defining moment in life. It defined one thing for me: that I would never look back and I would be successful and proud. Being proud was something I never thought I could obtain. It would take a few more years before I would get there.

System Shock

After graduation, I spent all of my time at home. It was the summer before university. I had applied to the American University of Paris, and I had been accepted into their Literature program. The plan was for me to leave in August. I was getting ready to say my goodbyes and I was trying to get accustomed to the idea of leaving my mother. I couldn't bear the thought, but I knew that I would never 'find' myself unless I left the Arab world. Looking back, I realize that I had found selves of mine, and right here, smack in the middle of the Middle East. I didn't leave to Paris. By mid-July, something very, very strange was happening to me.

I woke up one day feeling entirely numb. No, not emotionally numb, although yes, the lyrics of Linkin Park's 'Numb' sound very appropriate and very descriptive of the situation I was faced with. My limbs were numb; my arms, my legs, my stomach, my pelvic area, my back, my feet; and my fingernails. Everything. My first thought was that I must have overslept. I ignored the numbness. Hey, I was physically numb as well as emotionally. I could afford to be in denial. This went on for four days. I was slowly getting worse.

The numbness escalated and was starting to resemble paralysis. My most terrifying moment was the minute I looked in the mirror, found that my curls were rebelling even more than the usual, and I was unable to tame them. Brushing my hair was no longer an option. My fingers curled around the brush and it slipped right out of my hand. I stared at it as it landed on the floor. It seemed to mock me. I knelt down and fought with it; until I finally managed to get a grip. I calmed down once I was in control again. The process of brushing my hair was even more of a hassle. I just couldn't do it. It was best to pretend that it looked fine rather than dwell on my failed attempt.

There was no fooling Mom, however. Not for long anyway. On the fourth day, my Bad Hair Brushing Day, she walked into my room and opened the windows.

"It stinks in here. There's no air! How are you living? *Yalla*, you should go see a doctor. I don't think you should wait anymore. Doctors know best; go ask. I already booked an appointment for you. Get dressed!" She walked out of the room before I could complain and argue.

I drove myself to the hospital. How I managed that is beyond me. That drive to the hospital was possibly the most reckless and suicidal ever. My hands were on the steering wheel, I could see that they were, but I did not feel the movement of the wheel as it circled between my trembling fingers (they looked like they were trembling, but felt like sandpaper), and my feet were doing their job with the gas pedal and brakes. I drove in a complete daze, utterly disconnected from my body and reality. I was no longer Sarah. I was simply trapped in someone else's body, so I didn't panic. This was not my body. I just had to drive it to the hospital and wait for the doctor to probe at it and tell me what exactly was going on.

Notes on the Flesh

The Doctor was an old Egyptian woman, chubby, loud, and inarticulate. She was distracted by her mobile phone; it kept ringing as she stared at the screen, waiting for the caller to hang up. She wouldn't reject the call. I waited to be examined. She didn't irritate me at all, for some reason. I didn't feel as though any of this was real, let alone Dr. Samira. She was just a character. Dr. Samira did a routine examination of my body, my muscles, my ability to walk, checked my ability to react to stimulus, and if my vision was affected in any way.

"Humph." The sound of disapproval was the only noise that Dr. Samira uttered. She had pushed my arms down, after telling me to resist, and I had no strength. My arms flopped at my sides.

"I should refer you to another doctor. This really isn't my area of expertise anymore," she said, after reaching her desk. She began squiggling on a hospital notepad.

I nodded and thanked her. No questions asked. She placed the paper she had written in an envelope and sealed it.

"Here you go. *Inshallah* you will be better."

"Thanks Doctor. Have a good day," I said monotonously, as I reached for the envelope, trying so hard not to let it slip between my fingers. I focused on making sure that didn't happen.

As the door slammed shut behind me, I looked down at the envelope in my hands. It read: EMERGENCY: NEUROLOGY. I stopped in my tracks and scanned the hospital waiting room like I had just committed a crime. Guilty. Everyone I saw seemed angry. Bitter. Had I taken that long inside the doctor's office? 5:09. I hadn't spent ten minutes in there. But everyone looked more in need of a doctor's help. I was not one of the wailing babies, not one of the elders in wheelchairs, and definitely not pregnant. As far as they could see, I was a teenager who had nothing better to do than waltz into a doctor's office for a chat. I didn't blame them if they had thought that. Public hospitals and clinics were known to be frequented by people who had nowhere to be. There were people who would run to the doctor at the slightest hint of an upcoming headache. That's the thing about free health insurance. Like everything else, it gets taken advantage of.

At home, my parents insisted that 'EMERGENCY' meant actually going to see a Neurologist. We had two in the entire country. Dad dealt with the situation by scheduling an appointment for me and then said he would join me.

"How come you drove yourself to the first appointment?"

"I don't know," I replied. But I knew.

"That's nonsense. Anyway, make sure you wear something a little more conservative," he said, eyeing my jeans.

I never wear skinny jeans. The pair I was wearing was, according to River Island, "boyfriend's jeans." I never understood what that meant. Upon wearing them, did one acquire a boyfriend? Or, was I wearing my imaginary boyfriend's jeans? My thighs swam in their bagginess. There was no way the fabric accentuated any body part.

The car ride was very quiet. It wasn't that there was nothing to talk about. We could've talked about what would happen at the doctor. But we didn't and instead, avoided the topic altogether. Once we arrived at the doctor's clinic, we noticed that there was a separate seating area for men and women. There was a sign that clearly stated the rule. My father pointed at the women's seating area (in case I couldn't read) and I walked robotically to the only couch that was reserved for the ladies. I just wanted to sit down. There were two women sitting on the couch, so I took a seat next to one of them. Across the room, I could see my father fiddling with an old newspaper.

"*Salam*, why are you here? What's wrong with you?" the older woman asked. She was old and very thin with shoulders that hunched towards me as she waited for a response.

"I don't know."

"How don't you know? What do you mean? Do you have epilepsy?" She persisted.

"No – no, I don't. I don't think I do."

"Then what's wrong?" she repeated. Her tone was not gentle, but frustrated. She needed to know.

"Nothing is wrong with her. She's as healthy as a horse!" my father bellowed from where he was sitting. He had heard the conversation and had decided to take matters in his own hands.

"Ah, okay," she answered him, staring at me in disbelief.

I was very uncomfortable with the scene she made, or my father made. Or both. I rubbed my eyes, hoping I would bore her. But her interest refused to die.

"Sarah? Come, I must take your measurements," the nurse said. It sounded like a fitting for a dress.

She did just that though. My weight, my height, and of course, my blood pressure. She attempted small chat but I was nonresponsive and merely nodded my head.

The doctor was, as my father likes to say, a dinosaur. He was old, very, very old. He spoke in a very low voice, barely audible. After what seemed to be a routine examination, he concluded that I needed an MRI

(Magnetic Resonance Imaging). My father stared at him, obviously not happy with the request.

"Why should we do that?" my father asked.

"Because, we will be able to know."

"Know what?"

"What we need to know."

"What is wrong with her?"

"I don't know," the doctor said, sounding very much like me.

"And you will know only when we do this MR thing?"

"Yes Sir, MRI."

I watched their mouths as they conversed, wondering if I was expected to have a say in anything. I was fine with an MRI. Maybe I was dying.

"Doctor, is it bad?" I finally managed to croak out.

"It may be bad. But I don't know just how bad. There are a number of things."

"Like what?" my father barked.

"Sometimes, there are brain tumors that cause such symptoms. But not to worry."

"*Tumor*?" I knew what that meant. Who didn't?

"Yes. But if that is the case, we may treat it. You are very young," he responded, making sure to look at the door behind me. Maybe this was a way to detach from patients.

"She doesn't have a tumor. This is just stress," my father said calmly.

"We will have to see. Now let me write up the MRI request and once you get the results, bring them to me. I would suggest a private hospital, although it may be somewhat costly. MRI appointments usually take a very long time. They tend to be overbooked too, in public hospitals."

"That's fine; I will pay whatever is required. We just want answers," my father said gruffly.

The doctor busied himself as he wrote the request for the MRI. His handwriting, like all doctors', was unreadable in every sense of the word. But I could read the word "Urgent" and he had underlined it twice. I realized that there was no need to relay this information to my father, who had chosen to speak on the phone on the car ride to the hospital, instead of talking to me or acknowledging my existence. I felt invisible, just like I had felt at the doctor's office.

The MRI itself was an uncanny and strange experience. I had never been in that machine – it was very much like a white coffin. You get wrapped up in a blanket, like a baby, or a dead body, whatever you prefer, and are told not to move. Whatever happens, you cannot move. Hold still. Don't move your neck. Don't sneeze. Don't open and close your eyes. I wrestled with the orders, when told not to move, I wanted to move. When told not to sneeze, I felt my nose twitch. When told not to open my eyes, I felt my eyelashes flutter. I tried to calm my mind, telling myself to just try and listen to orders, just once.

"But, if you need anything, here's the bell. You just have to squeeze it," the radiologist said, placing the rubber 'bell' in the palm of my band.

"I will. Thank you."

"Also, you will hear a lot of noise. It's a very loud ringing noise. Some people prefer to listen to Qur'an, while others choose relaxing music," he said, placing headphones over my ears, and added, "it helps with the noise and stress."

"I think I'd prefer Qur'an," I said.

He nodded and left me, pushing a button that slid me into the machine. I looked above my head and really felt like I was in a coffin. I wondered what it would be like to be dead, yet awake, and hear everyone walking away from you, while you struggled to be heard. With that thought, verses from the Qur'an screeched in my ears. Now it really felt like I was attending my own funeral. Funerals have the Qur'an playing in the background. So I lay as still as possible, listening to the Qur'an against a backdrop of extremely loud ringing and buzzing. I winced as the pain and numbness in my hands was beginning to really infuriate me. I moved my fingers, opened and closed my fist, somehow hoping to regain feeling in them. But nothing changed. I persisted. Mom had always said that persistence cracks everything. You just have to keep trying, and above all, do not lose hope.

Suddenly, the radiologist entered the room. I heard his footsteps approach, and then his hand reach for the button, and I was sliding outside the coffin.

"You moved your head. And why do you keep moving your hand?"

"I'm sorry."

"It's okay, but please *try* to stay still. Also, does your hand hurt?"

"Yes," I whispered. I didn't think he could help.

"Okay, is it numb? Or painful?"

"Both." Numbness was painful. It wasn't as helpful as being emotionally numb, it didn't numb any pain. It wasn't a defense mechanism. It was just some sort of unexplainable mechanism happening to my body. It was just painful numbness.

"Hmm. Okay. Well, let's try again. Please be still." He pushed a button, and I was back in the coffin.

As I lay there, I thought of different things. I thought of life and death. I thought of my mother, of how much I loved her. But she wasn't here. And I thought of my friends, and how hurt I was. Then I thought of how all I wanted was to go back home and sleep. So I tried to sleep, but you really can't sleep with all that noise. I didn't care if they never found out what was wrong with me. All I wanted to do was go home.

About half an hour later, I finally did go home. The radiologist said that the results would be ready the next morning, and of course, not to worry. MRIs were like magic. They showed you everything that was happening in the human body. Especially the brain. And they had injected me with a solution that was specifically made to "color" the images. Everything would be crystalized and colored. There would be no more mysteries, and plus, I was young. They had kept repeating that, like age was a determining factor for everything.

My mother hugged me when I got home. There were no words exchanged between us. I climbed the stairs, watching as my feet attempted to function. It was all surreal and I found myself unable to even think, to analyze what was happening to me. I went straight to bed. The next morning, I woke up with a horrible headache. It was probably from all that ringing noise. But then I wondered whether it was become there something wrong with my brain, if I really had a tumor, could it be that something was causing my brain to rot? I text messaged my mother, complaining of the pain. I didn't want to have to say it to her face. It embarrassed me that I was in pain.

"Your dad took the results and went to the doctor's house to ask him what they mean. Don't worry," she responded.

My father had actually gone to see the doctor at his home? It was a Friday, which was probably why my father couldn't wait until Sunday morning, when everyone would be back at work. I dragged myself out of bed, fumbling to find my way, trying not to fall, to make sure that my feet were actually touching the ground beneath me. It felt like I was walking on air, and no, that was not half as pretty as it sounds. I wore pink fluffy pajamas and looked like hell -if hell looked like cotton candy.

My mother held me and said, "My baby. They want to keep you at the hospital for a week. They need to run tests."

I pulled away from her and said, "Mom, do I have to? Can't I run these tests and sleep at home? Please?"

I could see that she had tears in her eyes as she nodded. Then she firmly said, "I think you are right. You can do that. We will say that to the doctor."

So why hadn't you thought of that before, I wondered, but kept it to myself. As long as it was going to be okay. I didn't want to imagine sleeping in a hospital bed. That thought terrified me more than whatever was wrong with me.

Later that day, my father insisted that we travel to London. In London, doctors knew what to do, he said, and that would mean I would be 'okay.' I would be better off being probed by British doctors. I didn't refuse. I simply packed my bag (well, our housekeeper helped me pack it) and we were on the next flight to London, Heathrow.

The flight was torturous. A lady sat next to me with her wailing child and I couldn't get any sleep. I felt sorry for her but at the same time loathed her for having a child in the first place and putting him on the same plane. Suddenly, she flung the baby at me, where it landed on my lap, and asked me to please-and-thank-you hold it while she went to the bathroom. The baby and I stared at each other. It didn't cry at first, perhaps because it

Notes on the Flesh

was in the arms of a stranger. This was a weird baby, aren't they supposed to cry? Instead, the baby smacked my thigh so hard, I nearly screamed. At that moment, I asked myself a million questions. Why do people really have babies? Do I want one? (Yes, I asked myself that at eighteen), and more importantly, can I have one? What if my own baby smacks me? How do I deal with that? I won't be able to, for sure. It's not that simple. And does that mean I would be a terrible mother too? Mothers don't want to smack their babies back, do they? Unless maybe they have Post-partum. I'm told my mother was affected with Post-partum. I don't think she ever wanted me, or wanted to become a mother. It sort of just happened. Especially in the 80's. It took her forever to finally admit that to me. I think she felt that it would make her less of a good mother. What she didn't know, was that it made her more lovable, more human, more real.

I really wished she was there. I was traveling halfway across the world to some hospital; to do God knows what, with only my dad for company. We had never been close. It was more of an awkward relationship. But I was grateful that he had in fact paid for our flight to London, and that he was taking care of all the expenses. I knew he was always having financial difficulties. It's not like everyone in the Arab world is rich. Not even in the Middle East. He barely managed to pull through. I felt guilty for being such a burden – and I started worrying about all the money this situation would cost.

At the hospital, I was surprised to find that I was admitted as a Private Patient. Basically, that meant paying a lot of money. This was some sort of VIP section. Not that we had asked for it, but because I was an Arab, and I had no health insurance, there was no way I would get the same treatment as a British citizen. I was admitted and placed in a large private room, with a huge bathroom that had a bathtub in it. There was also a very small television hanging in the corner, and it scared me. It looked like it belonged in the eighties. It didn't fit amidst the sparkling clean room, the marble floors, the newly refurbished hospital, and certainly wasn't worth paying for. But it was the one item that caught my eye and it's the one thing I remember clearly. Black, the usual obvious color, but it was the oddest thing ever. And it taunted me all the time. I could see my reflection, lying sprawled on a hospital bed, a place I didn't belong in, a country that made me feel alienated, and a bed that rejected me. The English aren't half as hospitable as the Arabs are, and they really ought to smile more.

My father left me at the hospital and said he would be back later, in time for any tests they might be doing, any procedures they might preform. After he left, an Indian nurse explained to me that they would be needing to do a Lumbar Puncture, which is basically a test they do, where they stick a needle in your spine, extract some fluid, test it, and they find out whether you have Multiple Sclerosis or not. So far, the doctors were suspecting Multiple Sclerosis. At the time, I had no idea what that meant. It just sounded nasty. And the word 'multiple' meant it was going to be double trouble, and probably multiple disasters.

The doctor who performed the Lumbar puncture looked like David Beckham. He was stunning. He tried to make me as comfortable as possible, talking to me about all the places I should visit in London, the horrible weather, and where I was planning to study. I tried to talk to him, but I was too tense. I knew he would be sticking a needle in my spine, but I had no idea that it would hurt. Especially because he did anesthetize the area. I had my back to him, and I was curled up in a fetal position, while he was busy making sure he didn't paralyze me.

As the long needle entered what seemed to be the 'gaps' in my spine, I realized that somebody was drying my tears. I was unaware that I was crying. There were tears I was not aware of, running down my cheeks, and there were big, manly, hairy hands, hurrying to dry them, perhaps before I could notice them flooding my face and sob like a baby. I felt as though the world was ending. I stared at the empty space ahead of me, at the way the curtains seemed to dance in front of me, caught in a different world –a world free of pain. All I wanted to do was pass out. But there I was, still crying, as the beautiful doctor probed my spine.

When he was finished, I was told to rest and sleep as much as I could, and that a fever might visit me at night. I thanked him for everything, because you have to be polite, and say thank you for hurting me, because you're just doing your job and all.

I fell asleep immediately after, dozing off into a different place, a place where I was haunted by horrible nightmares, the kind that requires conscious effort to wake up from. I woke up screaming halfway through the night. I looked around me, and in the darkness, I realized I was completely alone. A nurse rushed in.

"I have to take your BP," she said, pushing me down. My head hit the pillow and it felt like it could smash into pieces.

So I lay there, and let her do what she needed. I tried to stay awake. I checked my phone and realized that my father had called and messaged me, apologizing for not being able to make it. My mother had also called me, so

I slowly, groggily, picked up the phone and pressed the Redial button.

"Hi Mama," I whispered.

And then she started talking, with that voice of hers, telling me that she raised a strong woman, and weakness is never an option.

"Stay warm. Stay in bed. And keep checking for any fever symptoms. Drink lots of water. It helps wash out the toxins," my mother ordered.

It took all the strength I had in me not to cry. I just kept saying yes, I will, don't worry, and I love you too.

"Did it hurt?" That was her final question. She had been avoiding it.

"Yes, but I am okay now."

"I am proud of you," she responded. That was the best way to end the conversation. We exchanged I love you's and goodnights.

I stared at the ceiling. It took me a few minutes to decide what to do. I think I had decided before I knew I had decided.

I called my best friend.

After six or seven times of calling Salma, her mother answered the phone. She told me that Salma was busy, but did I need anything?

"I just...wanted to tell her that I'm in London. I'm at a hospital. They think I could be sick. Something called Multiple Sclerosis."

"Oh! Oh no, no, I am sure that is not the truth. You don't look...you don't look MS, Sarah, you really don't. Those are old people. We had a relative who was in a wheelchair. You are so young dear!" Salma's mother assured me.

I didn't feel reassured. Instead, I felt as though she had just accused me of lying. Of exaggerating. Like I wanted to be old and in a wheelchair. While I spent the next hour fuming, Salma finally called back.

"Yes? How are you?"

"I'm okay. Thanks for calling back. I've been trying to reach you."

"Yes, I have been told. More than once."

"Well it was nearly impossible to get through to you. I am sorry. So sorry. I just am sorry," I apologized frantically. Perhaps if I apologized, she would be kinder.

"What do you need Sarah?" Her tone was ice cold. It was as though she wanted to spit on me, but her manners and upbringing did not allow her to.

"What do I need? What do I need, um, uh, well, the thing is, I am in London. But I'm at the hospital. I'm really sick."

"How sick?" Her voice remained the same.

"Sick enough that I can barely walk. I can barely hold the phone and talk to you. They don't know how bad it is, but it's bad, and I think it's chronic, and it has something to do with my brain, and maybe it's brain cancer for all I know, and maybe it's something called Multiple Sclerosis, which just sounds scarier if you ask me, and I don't know if I am paralyzed forever, or if I'm dying, but all I know is I'm scared and I'm alone... and I miss you so much, and I love you so much, and I just want us to be okay again, and if you'd just tell me what I've done to deserve this treatment, I would understand, and apologize, and we'd be okay. Please, Salma," I babbled.

There was silence. Just silence. And my heavy breathing. Or was it hers?

"I think I have nothing to say to that. Except that bad things happen to bad people. And you're evil, Sarah,"

Salma finally spit out. There. That was it. *That was all there was to it.*

There was a definite, large, lump in my throat. I couldn't spit it out. I couldn't get rid of it. I was silent, afraid my voice would crack.

"And that is all I have to say. But I do wish you all the best, and I have nothing against you, and I am sure you will be fine. Is there anything else you'd like to talk about?" Salma hissed.

"No – no. Thank you for your time," I replied, as formally as possible, and as untruthfully as ever.

And we hung up. But I never really got over it. I remained hung up. For the next eight years, her words haunted me, and I asked myself, what was it that made me evil? Did I really deserve to be punished? I didn't hear from Salma until years later. She eventually called me, eight years later, to apologize. She had decided to become a nurse and she worked with MS patients all the time. She claimed throughout all these years that her guilt kept haunting her. It turned out that there was one boy, one boy who used to go to our school, who had spotted her with her boyfriend. He had informed her brother of the crime he had seen, and her family had decided to blame it on me, to get her to confess. After all those years, it was simply because of some stranger's words, that everything had fallen apart.

A Decade Later

It only took Salma eight years to call me and apologize. Her job at the hospital as a nurse had acquainted her with different patients. She had come across cancer patients, patients with Parkinson's, and, unsurprisingly, MS patients. Because the US and Europe has a higher percentage of MS patients than Kuwait and the Middle East, it was inevitable that working in a hospital would entail coming face to face with them. Salma had managed to let go of everything pertaining to Kuwait, her family, her demons, her father's oppression, and yet, she was still haunted by the friendship of the girl who she had called Evil.

Working with patients had granted her a different view on life. She was able to view human vulnerability as a sign of greatness. The resilience of the human spirit inspired her, and she was sure that she had to make amends with me, find me, tell me that she was sorry. When she finally called me on my Kuwaiti line, I picked up the phone, unsure who was calling me from the US. The country code was staring at me, and I answered, wondering if I should.

"Sarah, it's me. Salma. Do you remember me?" she asked.

It's strange how people use this very generic question, do you remember me, as though we are able to forget those that pass through our lives, let alone people who hurt us, love us, or even share a meal or two with us. In Arabic, we have a word that is called *Ishra*, which means to live with someone, to share a life, to witness their paths. In Egyptian, they say we have shared "*aish* and *milh*" meaning bread and salt, and once bread is split into two, we cannot pretend that we never shared that intimacy. Food is an ultimate necessity, and to share it, to split it between two, is to establish, what seems to me, an irretrievable bond. I have always been aware of this strange predicament, and the way she asked me if I remembered her left me speechless.

"Good to hear from you," I replied, just as formally.

The conversation slowly shifted from a tentative hello, an uneasiness that demanded to be addressed, to a conversation about how our lives had turned out over the past ten years. She had built her life away from home, a new home that was granting her freedom, a home that was different from anything she had ever known. Freedom was what she had been missing all along. Her hair was finally breathing, she was no longer covered from head to toe, and she no longer had to pretend she was her father's daughter. She had become her own person. I was thrilled to know that she had managed to exorcise the demons of the men in her life.

And finally, as though she wanted to get it over with, she said that she was sorry.

"I'm sorry, I know I caused a lot of pain in your life. I know you are probably over it at this point, and maybe you don't even need this apology now. But you do have

Notes on the Flesh

to know that I was just a teenager, and a very confused one. I was manipulated by my family, and I needed someone to blame for all the pain I had to go through. You were the closest person to me, and there was no other person I could say let me down, except for you. You were the one who I could...I guess...bully," Salma said, speeding through her words.

As awkward as the apology was, I realized that I had to release both of us from the pain. I told her that it was difficult, but it was all good, and we were adults now.

"You don't understand. I spent years seeing your face in every patient's face. Every MS patient I met, I would look at them, and think about you. I would think about what I said to you. I made you feel like MS was your karma, like it was deserved...and that's just horrible. But I was a child. I didn't know that I was hurting you. I was just so frustrated and so angry at everyone," she continued.

"I do understand. I spent years hearing that verdict, that I was evil. I didn't understand why, and it was hard enough to try explain to myself why I got diagnosed with MS to begin with. I was searching for answers. Anyway, I do get it, and I appreciate the apology. I'm also glad you're working with MS patients."

"I work with them, yes. I work on their speech. You know MS patients, sometimes, they lose their ability to speak, or they slur their words. Are you suffering from this?" she asked.

"No, of course not. I don't slur my speech," I answered.

"Oh," Salma replied.

"Right," I answered.

I was not prepared to discuss my symptoms with her. This was a very private issue, and perhaps, on some level, I still felt as though I was deserving of a failing body. I didn't want to let her in on the secret that I do slur my speech, and that I was accused of being drunk many times before. The strangest part was listening to how her life had transformed and wondering how we were all just characters in each other's lives. Forgiveness was a huge word, a word that I was unfamiliar with. I needed to let go of the pain, of being bullied, of being seen as an outsider. I was made an outcast for something I had no part in, and after all this time, I was given an explanation and an apology. I took the apology, shoved it into my subconscious, asking it to shuffle the experiences, make sense of it all, and try to heal.

Intimacy and a Life-Bond

After the initial heartbreak of the MS diagnosis, I found myself uncomfortable in the presence of people. I was not capable of looking at people and not blinking excessively. This was yet another symptom I had acquired. My eyesight was blurry most of the time, and it was difficult to pretend to look normal. I felt afraid of the entire world around me, and I just wanted to protect myself from pain. I refused to cry, because I had been brought up to believe that crying meant a weakness of character.

I arrived back home from England, registered for university, and chose my major. My major would be English literature, like I had always wanted. My doctor had advised me not to bother with a university education, stating that MS is a degenerative disease. A disease that would eventually leave me bedridden. What good would an education do? Going to classes every day and driving to and from university would certainly only make my case worse. Although his "scientific opinion" sounded more like Quranic words, I chose not to subscribe to his belief system. I walked out of his office and decided that I could, at the very least, try to get through a semester. I needed the distraction.

The university I attended was a Public one. This meant that the student population was from all over the country, all social classes, and all religious backgrounds. Most of the female students were fully covered. I immediately felt out of place. My first class was a Basic English course, one that is a requirement. Everyone is required to take it, no matter what your level of English was. I was angry for having to attend this university. I had been accepted at the American University of Paris, and yet here I was, stuck at home. Anger swelled inside me and there was no mistaking it. I scowled at everyone who looked my way. There was no way anyone would think I was a good person, let alone an interesting person.

But then there he was.

That first class, amongst all the boys, there was one boy who stood out from the rest. The first feeling I had toward him was unexplainable irritation. I was completely annoyed with his existence. But let me take a few steps back and attempt to describe him. Everyone around us looked the same; everyone had the same features – everyone except for him. I fidgeted in my seat whenever he would turn around to speak to someone next to me. My fidgeting was perhaps an unconscious attempt to grab his attention. I stared at him like he was surreal, and simply, did not belong here. I forgot that I was a girl, and that I wasn't supposed to stare. I forgot all about cultural values and tradition.

We were required to introduce ourselves to the class. I never liked those introductions. I found them embarrassing and limiting. You get judged based on those two minutes that you try to describe yourself and

Notes on the Flesh

"who you are." My classmates all asserted that they were English majors because English was the number one language in the world. Others stated that they were very excited to finally be Freshmen. When it was his turn, he said that he was here because his parents worked here, but that he was supposed to study in Russia. His name was Ghazi, half Kuwaiti and half Russian. I guessed that his mother was Russian. The dark black hair stood stunningly against his white skin, and he reminded me of a vampire. Ghazi said that he was excited to be here and was hoping that University life would be more enjoyable than school.

Only two weeks later, after a marathon of constantly staring at each other, Ghazi approached me. He grinned at me and asked if I was a brilliant English major.

We were sitting in class, and I shuffled through my papers. I answered with a hesitant "Yes."

"So, would you like to maybe discuss Shakespeare sometime? Like, maybe, I could call you? We can practice different things. Or maybe we could just talk. About anything."

"Okay sure, but let's not talk about Shakespeare, Ghazi!"

And as though I was in a trance, not thinking about any implications, I wrote my number on the palm of his hand. I didn't care how insane or lame that was.

We both smiled at each other, and for the first time in forever, I felt my hand shake as I wrote my number on his palm. I pushed my fingers against his palm and said, "If it smudges, it's not meant to be. Don't open your hand for a few minutes."

We both walked away, he left campus, and I walked to my last class of the day. Dazed, I wondered what we would talk about. I was still unable to comprehend the intense feelings I had toward him.

Ghazi made me a CD of his favorite music. I believe he chose songs carefully as though he was trying to make a good impression. You can really tell a lot about a person from their choice of music. The first song on the CD was by Guns N' Roses, and it was titled November Rain. Years later, this song would remain engraved in my memory. The lyrics were all about love restrained, refrained, resisted, and repressed. And yet there is a hint of hope at the very end. Despite all adversity, there is a hidden hope. A flickering candle, a candle that could survive, despite all obstacles.

The next morning I put my best shirt on in anticipation of seeing him. When we saw each other on campus, he waited until I was alone to give me the CD.

"Hey," he smiled warmly at me.

I responded to his hello and immediately worried about the silence that would ensue. However, he quickly picked up his pace and began talking.

"My birthday was last week. I threw a party but I didn't invite you. I wanted to, but most people around here don't seem to mix. Guys and girls don't mix. And people here say that you're a bit mean and somewhat of a snob!" He laughed as though he disagreed with the 'people.'

"Hah! Well, Happy Birthday. I am not too surprised, people tend to dislike me. But thanks for wanting to invite me," I responded.

"I just don't think you're as mean and as tough as you seem. I think you're actually a softy. And I did want to include you. I don't want you to hear about the party and assume anything."

"It's fine, really. I'm not much of a party person. I actually hate dancing, parties, and any places where there are lots of people! Really, it's not my thing."

"Well, is music your thing? I have this CD that I like. It's just a CD," he said, darting his eyes away from mine as he handed me the CD.

"That is so sweet. I get to keep it?" I asked.

The bus was approaching, and we both knew it was time to go.

So what did I decide to do? I shook his hand.

He laughed at the action and replied with: "Let me know what your favorite tracks are."

The next morning, around nine am, I texted him: 'Good morning. In bed, tuned in to your CD. I like November Rain. It's sad, but raw. I think it's my favorite. What are you up to?'

I smiled at my phone idiotically when he texted back: 'Good morning beautiful. Yes, it is raw, but I think there's hope even when it seems like there isn't. Nothing, I'm enjoying the weekend.'

He asked if I wanted to join him and a few friends for coffee. Ghazi was very popular and had a group of mostly foreigner friends, or hybrids. Most of them were not even Muslim. I was hesitant, not knowing whether I would fit in with his friends. I finally mustered up the courage to call him and to explain.

"It's just, I tend to be awkward around people. So I hope you understand, although I'd love to see you, I think it has to be a no," I said.

"I do get it; I actually thought you would say that. Hmm, would you like to meet before? I have an hour to kill," he responded. His tone was hopeful.

And so, we did meet for coffee. He sat across from me, Starbucks mug in hand. The sun shone around his black hair, and I noticed, surprisingly, gray hairs scattered rebelliously. Each strand lit up on its own, and his eyes glistened beautifully as he looked at me, waiting for me to start talking.

"They're a different color in the sun," I said.

"What?" Ghazi looked confused.

"Your eyes, they look different in the sun. There's a hint of yellow in them."

"Oh. Thank you? I don't know, they're just eyes. People always comment on them. It feels weird. I guess I get them from Mom. Dad hates them, or hates me, I don't know. She passed away a year ago, and he can't seem to look at me."

"Oh. I'm sorry about your Mom. And about your eyes, I think naturally people would comment. They're different, and over here people have black or brown eyes. People always look at whatever differs from them. I guess girls fall at your feet," I said. I was trying to lighten the mood, as his face had grown darker, and the gray lights in his hair dimmed.

"I don't know. I don't particularly like it when they do! I guess they do fall. But here's the thing. They just fall for my looks. Once they hear about my mother being Russian, the relationship tends to go downhill. You know, family name, Elitism. There's a lot of stigma. Russian woman, was she ever really married to a Muslim man? You get all sorts of judgement." He looked at me for an answer.

"Yeah, I understand. I don't believe in idiocy and racism. Most of my friends were hybrids. I'm a hybrid myself, and I grew up bullied for it all the time. I'm sorry you did too," I said. Secretly though, I was glad he was on my team. He was like me, an outsider.

"You think you can have attraction before even speaking?" Ghazi asked.

"Yes, I think we don't necessarily have to use words," I said, suddenly feeling like a philosopher. But we were both comfortable speaking to each other. And that's when I realized I had to tell him about my MS. I didn't want to lie to him.

"Do you know what MS, Multiple Sclerosis is?" I asked.

"Yeah, my father is a medical doctor. I think it's like AIDS," Ghazi affirmed.

"Uh, no. Not AIDS."

"I really think it's like AIDS. Basically, your Immune System attacks you. Autoimmune Disease," he explained.

"Yeah. Well, I have MS." I looked him straight in the eye.

His expression changed. He was taken aback, and quickly realized his mistake.

"I'm so sorry. I didn't mean to say it was like AIDS. I actually don't know much." Ghazi said. His eyes were apologetic and he was embarrassed beyond words. His white skin betrayed him, and he flushed in humiliation.

"It's okay, you're the first person I actually told. I guess people will always react this way," I answered. And it did make me think. Would people always assume MS was just like AIDS? Did it mean I had done something sexual? Did it mean I deserved MS?

"Oh. Wow. Thank you for telling me. How long has it been?" Ghazi's tone softened, and his expression relaxed. He leaned forward in his chair.

"About a couple of months now."

"How do you feel now?"

"Fine, I'm fine," I said. This was incredibly strange, speaking about my MS to someone else. Someone who wasn't me. I hadn't even spoken about it to my parents. We never sat down and spoke about it the way I was speaking about it now. Somebody was actually asking me if I was feeling okay.

"I'll do my research about it, but please do tell me more when you feel like it. You're my friend. I want to know how I can help," Ghazi said.

"I don't need help," I fired.

"I didn't mean it like that. I meant if there's anything I can do..." he trailed off.

"Nothing, thank you. I just wanted you to know."

"I appreciate it, Sarah. I won't tell anyone, either."

"Please don't. It's top-secret. Nobody should ever know. My family would kill me. I'm not supposed to tell anyone."

"Why not? It's nothing to be ashamed of!"

"Yeah, I know, but try saying that to them. They don't get it. They worry, you know, that if people found out, I would never get married. And maybe my sisters won't get any suitors either. Because who wants to marry into a family with sick or disabled people?" I argued. I was speaking as though I was explaining the logic to both of us.

"Well, if someone decides to not marry you because you're sick, he's not someone you want to marry anyway. And you're beautiful and smart. You don't need to feel ashamed," Ghazi said, comforting my demons.

"Okay. But please don't tell anyone," I repeated. I tried to stay brave and not show him that I was a girl, that I would cry.

"I promised. It's our secret." He grinned at me.

And it became our secret for the next decade.

PART TWO

Voices of Lovers

Math and Randomness

Because MS is very random, very unpredictable in the course it decides to take, it can be even harder to explain to people. It is sometimes unusually difficult to describe the physical pain to someone who is not living in your body. It is just you, forced to make amends with your rebellious body. It will not listen to any commands. I was unable to explain any of my symptoms to people, or the crushing and chronic daily fatigue that was almost invisible.

But he was a fan of numbers. He claimed everything had a reason, everything could be predicted, analyzed, and outcomes could be avoided if one was prepared for all types of scenarios. He said he wanted to understand my pain, that he wanted to be able to empathize, but that he needed a manual of some sort. He needed to measure the scale of my fatigue, the scale of my pain, so he suggested that we work with percentages.

"Tell me the percentage according to how bad it is. Anything higher than fifty is a good day, okay?" she said.

"Okay. It's usually lower than fifty. But I like this. Let's do that," I replied.

And we did just that. He would be able to tell, just from hearing my voice. He quickly learned that I felt better in the morning than in the late afternoon, and that my voice became weaker as the day dragged on, that the percentage of my energy decreased as evening approached. With time, he was able to take one look at me and guess the percentage I was currently at. There was something comforting about being able to label pain, to identify it as real, as tangible, as merely a number. He said that everything in life needed measuring, that science was a huge part of our understanding of the world. I couldn't see it that way. I had long given up on science and doctors. Everything for me was abstract, unclear, and irrevocably vague. But his insistence on numbers made me feel less alone. Numbers were no longer the enemy. He loved numbers, and I surrendered. There is something beautiful about having someone witness your life's journey. A witness to pain, a witness to pleasure. The silence, leaning against the wall, watching, observing, knowing when to speak, when to breathe. There is an uncanny silence that affirms presence, and to be present, to exist, is to be, to heal.

The Ideal Woman

Mansoor had fallen in love with his high school girlfriend when he was only seventeen. They had dated in secret for nearly eight years. He had only touched her hand and kissed her cheek twice during the eight years. He was frustrated yet hopeful. He hoped that one day he would be able to marry her and finally culminate this love story. His lover, Noor, was very different. She was a good Muslim girl, and he was beginning to lose faith in a religion that organized the way people should love each other, and to what extent.

Being a conservative girl, raised in a conservative and religious environment, with parents who controlled her every move, Noor had adapted to platonic relationships. Her boyfriends all found her utterly stunning and made do with the fact that she would never touch them, never kiss them, and that they could only boast about her being their girlfriend. The physical aspect was completely absent from all her relationships. When he asked her how anyone could survive dating platonically, she was offended.

"Why not? Relationships aren't about sex!" she exclaimed.

"I didn't say that! I'm just wondering how it works, especially for men. Men have needs," Mansoor answered.

"Well, that's not my problem," she said.

"You're the girlfriend. You're supposed to be okay with it."

"I'm not! I can't be! First of all, it is a sin to let a man touch you, outside of marriage. You know that. And, I have my family's honor and my honor to protect. I am not one of those girls who just give their bodies to anyone!" she argued, her face turning blood-red.

"Why are you so angry about it? I think relationships should have nothing to do with honor. It doesn't make you a bad girl if you kiss your boyfriend. Do you know how many Arab girls do that? They actually do everything they can do, except lose their virginity. You can keep that!" Mansoor retaliated.

"I don't understand how you can be okay with it. Have you ever kissed anyone?!" she glared at him, her green eyes striking his very being.

"Yes I have," Mansoor responded.

"Because you're a man. You get to kiss as many girls as you want, fall in love so many times, experiment, and still get married without anyone judging you. You're not marked as a sinner!"

"Just a player," he responded.

"A player still gets a chance. A man gets way more chances than women," Noor argued.

"So are you saying you'd rather be with the man you eventually marry than the love of your life?" Mansoor growled.

"I'm saying I don't know if we'll ever have a family together. I'm saying I don't know if I'll ever be really yours," Noor whispered. She couldn't look at him.

Mansoor sighed. This was the argument of the past eight years. They had started out as two eighteen-year-old's, for the first time, struggling to make sense of a taboo relationship, a relationship that brought them satisfaction like no other, and yet at the same time, that very same love created immense psychological stress. They were living in a society where relationships between men and women were considered sinful if they were premarital. It seemed there was no hope for them at all. Mansoor was a Sunni and she was a Shiite. Doomed. His mother was also Filipino, and his facial features had marked him as an outcast forever, socially inferior. Her father would not have it, no matter how many times he proposed to her. And so it was, that their beautiful love ended up being in the realms of the unknown, thrown to the future, pending, undeveloped, and unfinished. Always on the periphery.

Mansoor would kiss her eyelids and apologize when she would cry. Noor always tried to hide her tears, but pleasure for her was heavily infected with guilt. Pleasure and guilt had become one. Mansoor wondered if she loved him as much as he loved her, and if she did, then why couldn't she just let go of God for him?

She swore that she did, that she had never loved anyone the way she loved Mansoor, with her whole soul, with her entire being. She said that he was her home, her sense of security, her backbone, the blanket that warmed her soul. Noor would hold Mansoor's face in her hands, look at him for a long time, and then say: "Never doubt my love for you. You can doubt God all you want, but never doubt my love for you. You should see the flame in my soul that burns for you. It will never stop."

So she loved Mansoor for as long as she could. Because everything stops at some point. There's an end to every feeling, to every event.

On a fateful day, her parents decided that she should meet someone – a man who had shown interest in marrying her. They felt that this man, whose name was Hamza, was a suitable choice. He was studying Medicine, and this made him a great candidate for marriage. What else could they ask for? It was important for them to ensure that their only daughter had managed to secure for herself a husband. A husband who would be fit enough to marry their beautiful and successful daughter. A modern arranged marriage. She could get to know him, speak to him, see him a few times, all in the presence of a male figure, her father or her brother Faisal would be there. What more could she ask for?

There she was, faced, for the first time, with a prospect of marriage. Her love for her mother surpassed any love she had ever known.

"If Mama is my sun, then you are my moon. I can't live without either of you. I can't disappoint either of you. What am I to do? Tell me, Mansoor," she pleaded.

But what was there to say? How do you tell the love of your life to go to someone else? How do you deal with that situation? Mansoor told her to try, for her mother, to try and give the man a chance. It didn't have to work out, but at least, she could say she tried. And then they would have their chance. He was still hopeful.

"The worst-case scenario would be if you marry him, get a divorce a few days later, and come back to me!" he insisted.

"You're crazy. How would I do that?" Noor was shocked with his lack of logic.

Mansoor insisted that it was in her hands to destroy this prospect, but that it had to be done carefully.

Reluctantly, Noor did go out with Hamza a few times. After every date, she would come back to Mansoor, crying. She began kissing him passionately, as though their first time would also be the last time. She held his face and traced every freckle, every acne scar, every emerging wrinkle, and said she wanted to memorize his face. When dreams are threatened, when the shadow of loss is nearby, people begin to resist. People begin to shake the bars of their cages. People begin to get angry. Noor was afraid of losing Mansoor for good. She tasted him as though she had been deprived of him for so long, like there was no return home.

She thought about the way she had grown up, always feeling suffocated. A caged bird. Noor had grown up in a very conservative home, but that was not the only issue. She was gorgeous, by many people's assessment. Her beauty was simply deemed too much. It was an excess of beauty. Her eyes were too inviting, her body was too seductive, her hair was too light, too golden, too different. She was gold itself, and because gold was hard to come by, everyone wanted a piece of her; including her parents. Everyone wanted to possess Noor, to keep her in check, to make sure she was behaving according to their rules. There was no room for her to ever speak up, to ever voice her own opinion or her beliefs. She grew up being told that she was a beautiful girl, and that she was extremely lucky to be so beautiful. What did girls need, other than beauty? In school, her grades never mattered. She had straight A's in History, English, Music, and B's in Math, Science, and Chemistry. But it was all the same. Her parents never cared, as long as she passed each year. The focus was always on her brothers, they mattered more, simply because they were boys. They would need a great job to be able to support their families one day, and they were the ones whose lives really mattered. A man could be ugly but a girl had to be beautiful, and the more beautiful she was, the better her chances in life were. And Noor had that covered. What did school matter?

She grew up fully aware of her beauty both at school and at home. By the time she was eighteen years old, she had started to loathe her body. Mirrors bothered her. And she simply couldn't believe that she was truly beautiful. Complimenting her failed most of the time, and she felt that anyone who complimented her was not being genuinely honest. Over time, she did come to terms with her beauty, but not after considering it to be a curse for most of her youth. Only through her love for Mansoor was she able to overcome her insecurities.

And yet, Mansoor was lacking. She loved him, but he was never the one who could protect her, who could stand up for her. As much as she loved him, he was marked, shunned. His mother, whom she loved, Elina, was part of the curse. Noor's parents would never approve. They were too elitist, too pure-blooded, and they would never settle for less than a perfect catch. More than anything, Noor wanted a chance at life. She wanted a baby. And she could never bring herself to voice the words to Mansoor. How could she break his heart? He was the man in her dreams, the man she felt safest with, and yet, his love was the most dangerous kind. There was no exit. Mansoor would never leave, and she knew it had to be her. She had to walk out.

She insisted that there was "no way out for a girl... we go from our father's home to our husband's." That was the sentence she used to defend herself in front of him. He attacked her mercilessly for being so weak. In his head, everything that happens to us is not simply because of fate. Fate is not completely, wholly, and irreversibly in charge. The universe negotiates. There are ways in which we can alter our oppressive realities. She called Mansoor an idealist, a hopeless romantic, and a selfish lover.

"How can love be anything but selfish?" Mansoor argued back.

"Love is selfless!" She screamed, over the phone, panting heavily, clinging to her definition of love, the definition that is somehow, universally agreed upon.

Love is selfless. Love means giving unconditionally. There's no limit to how much one loves. That's all he ever heard.

"If love was so selfless, why are you choosing the world? Why are you choosing to be with him? Why are you stepping all over me?!" Mansoor fired words at her like they could hurt her enough to change her mind.

And she never answered him. She never could answer him. When he questioned her lack of love, she said that they couldn't be young forever. That they had to grow up, that everyone had to get married in this society, that there was no other way to live. She believed that sustaining a hidden relationship would be impossibly heartbreaking – worse than leaving him for someone else.

"I already said yes to Hamza," Noor said quietly.

Mansoor froze. He had no words. He hung up the phone, and found himself hurling it across the room. Shattered. The pain was like nothing he had ever felt. By midnight, she had sneaked into his room. Like a baby, she tucked Mansoor into bed, and cradled him in her arms. She wasn't allowed to stay the night, but stayed until he fell asleep in her arms, drowsy and with the initial symptoms of a fever. Her arms rocked him back and forth, until the rhythm put him to sleep. He woke up to the sound of her voice, but she wasn't there.

Two weeks later, she was married. She had sent him a text message, saying that he should forget about her. She had the perfect wedding. A perfect image of the perfect girl. Was this the person Mansoor had loved for so long? It was a hidden love, only because she was too ashamed of it. He was her big secret because she had chosen to keep him there.

The Kingdom that they had created demolished right in front of his eyes. Everything turned to ash. There was no consolation. Nothing to say, no words that could make him feel better. The reality was he was powerless and unable to find a way out. She was still alive, breathing the very same air that he breathed, but she was no longer his. What kind of equation was this? Separation had actually happened. He had always believed that the time would come where she would be forced to get married, but that she would run for her life; that she wouldn't let them push her into anything. Mansoor believed wholeheartedly that Noor was not capable of being with anybody else. She was not comfortable with anyone, let alone her own self. How could she let another person touch her? How could she smile at the camera while she held on to Hamza's arm? It didn't make sense. He was going mad.

There comes a moment in life where everything you ever believed in comes crashing down, leaving you gasping for air.

Contract

Amal was very kind and easygoing. She was not used to making friends easily though. She kept her distance from people because she assumed having too many friends would simply be a headache. I found her strange at first. She was slightly older than me, in her early thirties, and we had met after years of being out of touch. I was shocked to find out that she had a daughter. Her daughter was twelve years old. Amal was divorced.

"I got married when I was seventeen. Love story, the usual mistake. I was divorced by the time I was eighteen. I gave birth and immediately ran away. He was abusive in every possible way you can think of," she said. Amal had deep brown eyes, and as she told her story, her eyes seemed to be shaking. A tremor took hold of her eyes, she was uncomfortable, yet she wouldn't look away from me.

"But at least you have a daughter. I love children, just can't think of having them," I said, wanting to steer the conversation away from the divorce story.

"It's not always a good thing. I love her, but it ties me down. I'm a divorced woman with a child. Forget the stigma that comes from being divorced, I'm also stuck with a daughter. Don't get me wrong, I love her – but it changes your life."

She was right. Society frowned upon divorced women, not divorced men. Divorced women were immediately branded as shameful, indecent, and women who were open to sexual advancements from men. Because they were no longer virgins, the stereotype was that they were open to sexual experiments and would even take money for it. Once divorced, it was very hard to lead a normal lifestyle. It was better to be single and never married than to be divorced and with a child. Amal was doomed, and yet I didn't want to be the one who confirmed it. I knew she already knew. But Amal, like her name, always had hope in a better future, in a better world, and in people. She had faith that everything would turn out okay in the end. She didn't believe in giving up. Life had not beat hope out of her yet. She was still beating on, against all odds, and wanted to believe in her perfect fairytale ending. She was in love with a man who had never married, was a perfect catch, and he had been honest with her from the very beginning of their relationship. Abdulghafoor told her that he could not disappoint his mother. His mother would never agree to this marriage, she had always hoped that he would marry a "perfect girl." Because he was the eldest amongst his siblings, Abdulghafoor wanted to please his mother, even though her overwhelming affection suffocated him. He felt as though he owed it to her to make her happy.

"What about you? How can he choose to make his mother happy and yet break your heart?!" I asked Amal.

"I have to believe that he won't be able to break my heart. It's been seven years, and he hasn't been able to walk out yet," she whispered.

"But it's a waste of time. A waste of youth. You could meet someone who will love and accept you, embrace your daughter, and want to give you what you deserve. It's not your fault you're divorced."

"It's not my fault, but I am flawed because of it. I'm the one with the issue, not him. He's perfect."

"He's not perfect. He's a coward. Listen, he's a man. Abdulghafoor has all the tools, yet he simply won't fight for you!" I exclaimed. I was out of breath, and I felt as though I had crossed a line.

Amal stared at me politely. After a long pause, she said, "Sarah, thank you. You said what I keep thinking, but I don't have the words or the nerve to say what I really feel. I feel so guilty about being not good enough for him."

Our society was obsessed with perfection. Everyone strived for perfection, for idealism, for a perfect image, no matter how much suffering it entailed. Stigma was everywhere. People continued to disappoint, regardless of gender, social status, and illness. I remembered how two years ago, I was approached by a young man who wanted to marry me. Rami had fallen in love with me after seeing me only once. He was a friend's brother, and like all arranged marriages, he claimed that he knew I would be his wife.

At the time, I tried to give Rami a chance. But there was a catch. When I told Rami I had MS, he panicked. He couldn't handle the idea of it. His first reaction was: "What about kids? Will they get it too?"

I explained that there was no scientific evidence that MS was genetic. And yet he insisted that the risk was high, and he wanted to make sure he had healthy children.

"How do you know you won't be in a wheelchair a few years from now?" He was very straightforward.

"I don't know. How do you know you won't be in one?" I frowned.

"Well, my chances are lower. I may not be completely healthy, but I don't have a risk as high as yours. I don't know if I can see you in a wheelchair."

Rami needed constant consolation. He needed to be reassured that I would be okay, that I wouldn't disappoint him. He made it seem as though he loved me so much that he couldn't bear the thought of me being in pain. When I went home to tell my parents about it, I was met with conflicting reactions.

"A man has the right to know what kind of mother for his children he will have. This is marriage, it's very serious. Don't be angry if he isn't sure about you," my father said.

"People don't understand your illness. You can't expect them to jump right in. He has his doubts, and it's your job as a woman to comfort him. Make him feel secure," my mother added.

"What about me? Who makes me feel secure? Am I supposed to beg him to marry me? You guys just want to get rid of me!" I barked.

"No, of course not. Your home is always with us *Baba*, it's not about that at all," my father said. But I knew better. He was worried his daughter would never marry.

"You don't have to marry him Sarah. It would just be better for everyone if you did," my mother insisted.

"I feel as though I'm convincing him to marry me *Mama*," I said.

"Don't think of it like that. Try to look at it from a different perspective. You might have a family, and lovely children. He's a good man, he's just afraid."

"Children. I don't know if I want them, or if I can even have them. I'm in pain most of the time, how can I handle carrying a child?!"

They were both silent. Finally, my father concluded the conversation by saying that it was all God's will. Whether Rami decided to marry me or not, whether I would always have MS (he still believed someday I would be cured), and whether I would have healthy babies or not. There was nothing anybody could do, we had to leave it up to God.

But that same night, Rami had a panic attack. He was struggling with anxiety related to my illness and having to deal with it. He had spoken to his mother about marrying me, and she had flat-out refused. She would not have any "disabled girls" in their family. He repeated to me the entire conversation between them, letting me know that she did have a point. She was afraid that her grandchildren would be disabled, and she wasn't willing to take any risks. She told her son that she would find him the best girl in town, someone even better, healthier, more beautiful, and worth marrying.

I was furious. I didn't even want to marry him, and here I was, marketing myself. I felt like a product that had to be sold before its expiry date. And yet I didn't want to be sold. I finally took a step and broke things off with Rami. I wasn't going to put up with it anymore.

"Let me make it easier for you. I don't want to marry you either. I don't feel comfortable being with someone who makes me feel like he's doing me a favor by marrying me," I affirmed.

"But it's not a favor. I'm just not sure. I don't think I can handle it. I'm not that strong. You are," he answered.

And he didn't want to be "strong" either. It fascinated me how the best excuse to every disappointment is that the person doesn't have what it takes to fight for you. Like Abdulghafoor, Rami gave up too soon. Marriage was a social contract, a contract that made no sense to me at all. It was about products, about how good the goods were, and whether you were worth purchasing. When I walked away from Rami, I felt a certain sense of pride. I had done what I wanted. I wasn't begging him to marry me anymore, and I didn't have to prove my worth to him or his mother.

I wanted the same for Amal. I wanted Amal to have someone who would fight for her, someone who wouldn't be ashamed to choose her. But Abdulghafoor couldn't choose her, and they struggled with many breakups throughout the years. Amal was sure that Abdulghafoor would come back to her, because love never ends. She believed wholeheartedly that love didn't just disappear, that people only lost their way, but that did not mean they would always be lost. Time was the answer to everything.

"Time makes people realize what they lost. They always come back. The secret is, you have to keep holding on. *Save the best image of your lover in your head, never doubt the love. That's what love is all about,*" Amal insisted. And, throughout the years, I never saw her change her mind.

An Encounter

"A re you happy?" I asked her. I was still unsure what she was doing flirting with me. She had a partner. He wasn't her husband, but they were in a committed relationship. I was recently divorced, and I wasn't up for the hassle of yet another heartbreak. My wife had left me because I was infertile. It was a mutual decision, and it had been a year since the divorce. I was slowly beginning to get used to the idea of being alone for life. What use is a man if he can't give a woman the one gift she waits for all of her life? A baby. That's all there is to it. A baby. The entire meaning of life, summarized in the face of a child. I had failed at that, and I was certain I would never find love again. I wasn't even sure I was looking.

"Yes," she replied, too quickly, interrupting my thoughts.

"Okay, on a scale of one to ten, ten being the happiest, what would you say?" I asked.

"Ten," Maha stated.

"Right. So maybe we shouldn't be having this conversation?"

"Perhaps. It's just you're so easy to talk to. But yes, I agree, I should avoid this. Anyway, I am sorry about all this."

We hung up the phone, and I thought that would be the end of it, again. A few days later, she texted me asking for my home address. I gave it to her without thinking. I thought maybe she had changed her mind and that she wanted to see me. But instead, she sent me five boxes of chocolate. Her rationale was that she wanted to do something for me. I was taken aback.

And then I asked her out for water. Not for coffee, because she didn't drink coffee.

"How about just water?" I asked.

"Water. Water is always good. Never been asked out for water though, are you stingy or something?" she teased.

"I just really think we both need water," I replied. I felt like I was a character in a movie, and I was coming up with the cheesiest lines.

She refused to go out with me, but it wasn't a flat-out rejection either. She said the infamous words "we'll see." I hated we'll see. See about what? Who's we? Why is there a "we", and why is there a subject to ponder? The best solution was to devise a place in which I would "run" into her "randomly." I knew where her gym was, and I knew there was a café right across the street from it. I took my books and decided to sit there, hoping she would be around. I waited for hours before I let her know that I was at the café, and I wondered if she would like to join me. Surprisingly, she said yes.

I sat there, drinking my tea, waiting for her to arrive. I thought about how I would react when I'd first see her. I had butterflies in my stomach for the first time in years. I felt like a teenager, and I was nearly thirty-five at the time. She arrived a few minutes later, barely giving me time to revel in my panic.

Her wild hair announced her presence, as her strands flew around her face. She had tied a sweater around her

Notes on the Flesh

hips, and her curves were impressively seductive. She took off her sunglasses and at once, I was hooked.

"I can't believe you have to see me like this," she said as she sat down across from me.

"What's this? You look good," I said. I didn't know where I got the courage from.

She stared at me and I looked back at her. There was something about the way we always looked at each other. We both couldn't look away, and even though I was fidgeting on the inside, I remained still the longer she looked at me.

"I should go, I can't stay that long. I have a business dinner to go to," Maha spoke softly this time. It was as though she didn't want to leave.

"I understand. I'll see you when I see you," I said. We said goodbye, and she texted a few minutes after, asking me: "How come I feel like I know you? It's like I haven't just met you."

It sounds cliché. It sounds like I'm making it up. It sounds like she used a very common pick-up line. But I felt exactly the same way. I was at home with her. I was comfortable, and I was able to relax. For awkward people, relaxation around strangers is next to impossible. But here I was, capable of sitting down with her, flirting with her, and opening up to her. I knew what she was talking about. And yet we were both afraid of the situation. It took a few days for us to discuss what we were feeling towards one another. We were fully aware that there was insane chemistry between us, but she just couldn't do anything about it.

"My partner, he's good. He's very good to me. There's nothing wrong with him," she explained, almost to herself.

"Then what's this? Then why me?" I asked.

"I don't know. He's not you. There's this strong pull towards you, I can't resist. The way you speak, the way you look at me, the way I can talk to you. And I'm attracted to you, mentally and sexually," Maha whispered. She was so brave, to say all that, I thought. How could someone just tell it as it is?

"So what happens next?" I asked. I needed answers.

"I can't cheat on him. I just won't do it. I can't have an affair with you. But God knows I'm trying so hard to resist."

And that was how the situation evolved from mutual interest to a very passionate affair. When people label their feelings, when emotions are put out there, when passion is voiced, it suddenly becomes a story with multiple layers. The minute we acknowledged the mutual interest, the relationship took on a different flavor, a heightened level of attractiveness. The desire was pronounced. We started speaking as though we had never dated anyone in the past. We opened up to each other over late night phone calls, and I couldn't help but wonder where her partner was at the time. Yet I didn't ask. I didn't want to ruin my fantasy. I pretended that there was no partner for the longest time. I liked the way we barely got enough of each other, because we were always limited in time. Time was a determining factor in this relationship. This was the woman that helped me understand myself. She explained me to myself, as though she had the manual to my mind, and I was always listening carefully to the way she picked at my mind, slowly dissecting it, revealing its intricacies, soothing its traumas. She made me feel like I was a man, whole, and complete.

As we continuously attempted staying away from each other, the attachment level grew. We were constantly avoiding each other's presence. That seemed fine by me, for the longest time, because I was afraid of commitment, and I felt unworthy of being in a relationship with anyone, let alone someone as perfect as she was. She was healthy, rich, fit, and on top of the game. There wasn't anything she was missing. Even the car she drove was a flashy Porsche. Everything about Maha was extravagant. She loved materialism, shopping, collecting strange and unique gemstones, diamonds, and jewelries. In short, she was an "uptown girl" and led a very extravagant lifestyle.

Maha kept repeating to me that she wanted to be with me, but was unable to break her partner's heart. She couldn't leave him without a "real reason."

"A real reason? How about the fact that you met someone you connect with?" I yelled.

"Salim, would you rather I just left him for no reason? Would you trust me if we get together? You'd always think to yourself, Maha will leave me for the next best thing. I know you won't be able to help it," Maha answered.

"I trust you, I do. We will be fine," I said, trying to convince her.

"And it's not even about children, you know that. I don't want children. I'm almost forty. I don't have the same desires that other women do. I just don't want to hurt him," she explained.

"And you'd rather hurt me?" I fired.

"I'm just so confused," she replied.

We hung up the phone, having reached no conclusion. A few hours later, I found her parked in front of my apartment. I didn't know if she wanted to join me in my car, or whether I would go to her, but I knew she didn't want to enter my apartment. She had always been scared of taking that step. So I stayed in my car, while she pointed at the house. I understood. Today would be the exception to the rule.

"Hi," Maha said the minute we were both standing in front of our cars.

"Hi," I repeated.

There was a strange communication between us. Our "hi" always meant more than just a hi. *It was an acknowledgment of each other's presence.* When we would argue, she would interrupt me halfway through to say hi. When I missed her, I would say hi. "Hi" was our own. It confirmed that we still cared for each other, despite the lack of commitment, despite the relationship not going further. Before each hi, there was an overpowering silence, a state of breathlessness that demanded recognition. We could never stop staring at each other. It was as though we were both completely taken aback by each other's energy. It was a state of complete stupor, I felt as though my brain had split from my body, and I was viewing myself from a different angle. I could hardly recognize myself, and I was not sure if I was imagining that she was feeling the same. I kept trying to deny the devastatingly beautiful effect she had on me.

But by the time we were indoors, Maha reached for me. I froze.

"Hey, Salim, it's okay," she whispered. I was sitting on the couch next to her, and she had grabbed me slowly, pulling me down onto her lap.

I was crushed. I hadn't been touched by anyone in so long. And here was this beautiful, surreal woman, telling me to put my head down on her lap. She rubbed my shoulders, re-assuring me that it was okay. Her eyes filled with tears when mine did. We sat there in silence, neither of us daring to say a word. What was there to be said? We both felt at home with each other, and we both recognized that this was no longer a simple infatuation. She had come to me. Why was it that she had turned to me, and how did she end up here? She was a smart woman, there was no doubt. All her actions and decisions were premeditated and calculated. Had she really made a mistake? Was I just a mistake? I simply wanted to be with her. She was my missing puzzle piece, and I wanted to seize it will all my might.

The room was pitch black, and Maha's black hair surrounded me. Her breath on my neck held me in place, and I reached for her back, tracing my fingers along her spine.

"Where does it hurt?" I asked. She had told me that she had back problems. Once, it was so severe that she was left unable to move for days. "A bit lower than where your hand is," she replied, "there you go." It was at the bottom of her spine. I couldn't imagine her in pain. Was she as human and as flawed as me? I didn't want to think she ever suffered either. I despised the human body in all its viciousness and its unexplainable wrath against us. I hated the way I could not provide her with anything. She would stay with her partner, and I would remain distant from her.

The affair ended, and we both went our separate ways. I ended up moving from one woman to the other, from one attempt at love to another. They never committed to me, and I am not altogether sure I was looking for a commitment. Marriage was no longer on my list. After Maha, I was sure I would not find love. She never married Nader anyway (I found out his name was Nader), and yet, we both couldn't reach out for the other. She felt as though she had committed adultery, and that I had assisted in the crime against the good man, Nader. She couldn't bring herself to see our love for what it was. And I let my ego take hold of me. *I forgot about her, forgot the way I thought she was the only love I wanted, and I went on with my days, sinking deeper into the robotic lifestyle I adopted.*

Ishq[2]

I couldn't understand the feeling I experienced when I first laid eyes on him. His face was as striking as the sun's bright rays, demanding to be let in, while you try so hard to hide under the covers. But the sun still shines through, through the curtains, through to you, and finally, after resisting, you find yourself climbing out of bed, and finally, reluctantly admit that it *is* a beautiful day. I never wanted to admit that he was the most beautiful person I had ever seen. Everyone around us looked the same; everyone had the same features – everyone except for him. He wasn't dark or broody and had no sense of humor. He just was. There. Present. His nose was pointy, like an eagle's. His jet-black hair curled at the nape of his neck, and his broad shoulders reminded me of a lost home. I was always nostalgic for him. There was no going back. The second I laid eyes on him, I shook my head, as if attempting to shake him off. *A decade later, I was still trying to shake him off.* Two children later, I was still nostalgic for him.

---

[2]   In Persian "ishq" means love.

My mother told me that Bader would never marry me. Bader's father was a religious fanatic. He believed women were to be covered from head to toe, and he believed that he could force his children to be replicas of him. Bader refused to follow in his father's footsteps, but he couldn't fight him either. Over the years, he grew a beard, and he was forced to pretend that he was praying five times a day. He wanted his father's approval. He was his eldest, and he could not imagine breaking his heart. So he went through the motions. He pretended to pray. And he prayed for courage, for the strength to break his father's heart. To tell him that he was in love with me, a liberal girl, a girl who refused to wear the hijab, a girl who lived on her own abroad, a girl who was branded a feminist. I was everything his father feared. My war was against patriarchy and oppression, and the man I loved was struggling to fight the same war. I felt abandoned in every sense of the word. Bader couldn't leave me. He never could say goodbye. And so it was, that I had no other choice but to cut the cord. We were dancing around each other, unable to move on, unable to let go. A dance that could only end when one of us stopped following.

After I finally left him, I struggled to build a new sense of identity. Was I happy? I don't think I have found happiness. But when I look at my daughter's face, knowing that she will never have to pretend, knowing that she will not have to bow her head to a man, to authority, I think I made the right decision. I was madly in love with Bader, my Bader, the moon, the beautiful moon that made everything even more wonderful. But Bader couldn't shine hard, he couldn't speak up. He spat his father's words at me: "I won't shame the tribe. Your hair is there for everyone to see. You refuse to hide, you refuse to see the taboo that it is."

I refused. I didn't budge. I wanted to extend my arms to him, to be his wife, to be his lover, his mother, his friend. I was the mirror to his soul, to his words, but he couldn't reconcile faith with culture, freedom with tradition, intellect with oppressive ideology. And as much as there was undying loyalty between us, I realized that my loyalty was to my unborn daughter. I left Bader and left a part of my soul with him. Sometimes, I look at his picture on Facebook and search for the light in his eyes – I am left with nothing but my delusions. *Was he ever as bright as the Sun, was he ever who I thought he was?*

Death and Rebirth

There was a new experimental surgery. It was not meant to be performed on all patients, it was reserved for cases that really needed help, and people who could afford it. The surgery was performed by an Indian doctor who claimed to have found a cure for illnesses like Cancer, MS, Epilepsy, and other auto-immune diseases. He was, in a sense, performing it illegally. I was desperate for any cure at this point, and like all chronically ill patients, I would have done anything for a cure, even it was a pseudo-cure. I was acutely aware that this surgery would be risky, but I chose to blind myself to anything other than the distinct hope that there could be something, anything, that could save me. I found the doctor after an intensive Google search. Ghazi and I argued about my decision to experiment. One day, the phone rang. The doctor spoke to me about how much the surgery would cost, and he urged me to think about it very seriously.

"There are no other options for you. You are very young, and could possibly recover. You have one shot at life. If I were you, I would understand that my options, in Western medicine at least, are very limited. The West does not want to cure Cancer or MS, all these diseases are politicized. You must take charge of your life. Don't worry, you are in very good hands," he insisted.

Dr. Parvesh was certain that stem cells were the answer to everything incurable. I didn't even really understand what stem cells were. My research indicated that stem cells meant younger cells, cells that were fresher, better, more capable at fighting disease. There was one slight problem. Cells could multiply. I was a Literature major, and I didn't understand the mechanisms behind this multiplication.

"Cancerous cells, Sarah. Cancerous cells. It means there's a bigger risk here," Ghazi explained, saying that he had done his research.

We were only twenty-three at the time. We were hoping to start our lives together, and yet there was a threatening life or death situation. We argued about the possibility of cancer. We fought about Quality of life versus Quantity of years.

"I don't really care," I said bluntly.

"So you're suicidal now? You want to just…die?"

"No, I want a proper life. I'm tired of being like this. I'm not even thirty. Who cares about how many years I live?"

"That's suicidal."

"That's not. It's not that simple, again, you never really get it."

"How can I not? I live with it every day."

"There's still a huge difference between you and me. You don't suffer half as much," I said these words carefully. It was the first time that I had voiced my alienation. It wasn't his fault I felt this way.

"I can't lose you. Please don't do this. You're giving up the fight. I didn't take you for a quitter," Ghazi responded.

Finally, we decided that I should approach my parents with my decision. I wanted to inform them, I didn't want an opinion. My parents had continued to be in denial about my health. My mother, when pressured to listen to my logic, said that she needed to speak to the doctor. She wanted to hear it from him instead.

"Money won't be the issue. I will sell everything I have, if it means buying your health. Stop worrying about that *habeebti*," Mama said.

My eyes were brimming with tears. I had support. I had at least secured the financial support. There was no way I could afford this surgery otherwise. My mother was not rich, and neither was my father. I was not sure how she would afford paying for my surgery. I didn't want to burden them any more than what they were already dealing with.

"I promise I'll save money, I'll pay you back, I won't forget this ever," I blubbered.

And so it was that my surgery was done in a very remote area. It was done in a deserted hospital in an Indian city. Ghazi and I went together, because neither of my parents were willing to be there for it. We packed one bag with both of our clothes and a few novels to read. Leo Tolstoy's *Anna Karenina* was a favorite of ours. Anna's character fascinated us, and her affair with Vronsky reminded us of forbidden loves. Even Russia had its conservativeness. So it wasn't just us. Can you control who you love? Can you always do what is considered right by the eyes of society? Anna couldn't. But then again, Anna's story was a tragedy. Were we the same? His mother and father had married. He was just not sure how his father would allow him to marry a Bedouin girl, a girl from a tribe, and worse, a girl who was struggling with a disability. His father, being a medical doctor, believed that chronic illnesses and disabilities were a burden, a curse, and that most "normal" people would not be able to live intimately with an ill person. He worked with patients every day, and yet, he was phobic of all illnesses, all degeneration of the body. He obsessed over Ghazi's health. He had lost his wife to cancer, and he couldn't bear the thought of losing Ghazi. According to Ghazi's father, cancer was definitely genetic, and Ghazi's mother had passed on the cancer gene. It was just waiting to make its dramatic entrance, seize Ghazi's body, and take him back to his mother's womb.

Although we knew that his father would never support us, we didn't care much for it. We were simply teenagers, trying to make sense of the world around us, and we had decided that we would never think about marriage or real life. We would take it all one step at a time. I was starting to feel hopeless and helpless, but I was more immersed in my failing body, than the prospect of a failed love. My mind could only handle one loss at a time.

But if I thought our love was tragic, nothing could have prepared me for the surgery that killed me. I was killed and brought back to life. The theory was, in simple terms, that the body's immune system had to be reset. Cells would be extracted from my body, from bone marrow, from my blood, and later infused back into my system. But not without the risk of death and not coming back to life. Of course, there was an agreement to sign before anything was to happen. I had to sign that I was not allowed to sue the doctors and that I could not turn to any medical organizations for assistance. This was completely on me. There was a lot of legal jargon written, which I admit, I didn't read. I took the pen and signed, eager to start a new life. Eager to be re-born, eager to have the better and healthier body I wanted.

"No, don't sign," Ghazi argued, the second the pen was in my hand.

"I have to," I answered as I scribbled my initials.

He was afraid, I knew that he was, but he tried to remain as composed as possible. He wanted to pretend that everything was under control. When they started prepping me for surgery, we were surprised that it would not be in a very sterile environment. There was no operating room. It was an outpatient clinic. Ghazi glared at me and then at the doctors. I shrugged my shoulders at him, helpless, refusing to entertain the thought that this could be dangerous.

When the surgery started, I was told that I would remain completely awake. Dr. Parvesh and his two assistants hovered over me. One of them was not dressed in a lab coat, and I wonder now if he had even washed his hands. He was old and looked very gruff. The first part of the surgery included the insertion of two huge needles in each arm, and Dr. Parvesh attached me to a machine that was supposed to separate the blood cells. I felt as though I was being crucified, arms stretched out, attached to a machine, not allowed to move at all. Any movement would only cause the needles to dig in deeper. I tried to remain as strong as ever. My muscles started to ache about half an hour later. Slowly, I began shivering. As I was being emptied of my blood, literally being sucked dry, my body temperature dropped drastically. Ghazi noticed my blue lips and nearly swooned.

"You're not okay, don't lie to me, you're not okay," he said.

"I'm fine," I said through chattering teeth. I couldn't stop shaking. I wanted to stop shaking so bad, but I couldn't. Dr. Parvesh only piled more blankets on me. They were green, wooly blankets. Blankets that smelled like death. Rotting, everything was rotting. I could taste metal in my mouth.

In the next four hours, I continued to suffer. I lost my ability to see, and could barely hear what was happening around me.

"I can't see! Ghazi, I can't see!" I screamed.

"She can't see! Do something!" I heard Ghazi scream at the doctor.

"No worries, it's all part of the process. She will be fine," Dr. Parvesh's assistant replied.

"She's dying," Dr. Parvesh said, slowly, as though I couldn't hear him.

"What?!" Ghazi was losing it. I couldn't see him, but I felt his body shift from my bed, heard his footsteps as he crossed over to the other side of the room.

I was, in fact, dying. My system was shutting down. I began to see darkness, and there was no beautiful white light. It was nothing like the stories I had heard. This death entity was not terrifying. I was ready to go, I simply wanted the pain to end. I was exhausted, and all I wanted was to rest. I thought of God. I thought of vampires and blood. And then I let go.

I am told that I was gone for about five minutes before I was resuscitated. The doctors had to use electric shock to get my heart to start working again. In the meantime, I have no memory whatsoever of death. I don't recall seeing angels, and I don't recall speaking to anyone. I only remember being ready for death.

When I was back, Ghazi was next to me, shaking with terror, convulsing in fear, his face panic-stricken and streaming with tears. He was sobbing, calling for God, and me.

Notes on the Flesh

"God! God please save her! Please don't take her away! I'll be good, I promise, please don't take her! Sarah!" Ghazi was a nervous wreck, and I felt nothing.

I coughed a few times, my eyes watery, blurry as my eyesight came back. Vomit gushed out. Dr. Parvesh's assistant stared at me, while Ghazi reached over to wipe my mouth with tissues. He put his hand on my head, repeating words from the Qur'an.

"Sir, I might have to ask you to leave. You are making this so much worse," Dr. Parvesh said calmly, as he injected me with something else.

"I will not leave. I don't trust you one bit. When will this be over?!"

"In a couple of more hours. Relax. The worst part is over. She's still here. As new as a baby. Her cells will be new, her body will be rejuvenated. You should remember this day forever. You'll always celebrate it as her new birthday," Dr. Parvesh said proudly.

"Make it stop," I whined. I wanted the needles out.

"Be brave, you're nearly there," Ghazi answered me, through gritted teeth.

I looked at him with pleading eyes. He was the only one who could speak on my behalf, the doctors would listen to him. I needed to convince him. But he glared at me harshly, refusing to budge.

"Please, Ghazi make them stop. I can't do it anymore. I don't want it anymore," I whispered.

"No. Don't do this. You wanted this, and we will get through. Stop nagging!" he screamed.

We endured two more hours of me groaning in pain, cussing at the doctors, and begging God to release me, to end the pain. I must've done all kinds of bargaining. But I survived. They removed the needles and stuck in the last one, the final one, the one that supposedly had the new cells that would be delivered into my bloodstream. That process was painless, and I lay there, slowly regaining strength. I thought of mortality and immortality. I wondered what kind of God existed. If he did exist, why had he let me suffer, only to bring me back? Was this a test, a punishment, or was I blessed to live? Whatever the answer was, I didn't care. I felt expelled from the entire universe.

That night, I lay in bed staring at the ceiling. When I finally slept, I had nightmares of needles, torture, blood, and dogs biting into my flesh.

Ghazi left me a few days after the surgery. He couldn't go back to the way things were between us. Everything reminded him of blood. Everything reminded him of pain. I was healing, but he couldn't see past the pain. There was only darkness.

"And this is all out of love for you, you have to understand this. It was so traumatic, I don't know how to move past it," he whispered. He was reminded of the loss of his mother, and he thought that his father might have a point. His father' advice was to never get too close to disease and illness, because it contaminates, not just the body, but those surrounding the patient. Ghazi wanted me to understand that he was too horrified, that he wanted to try and establish a normal life, and that he needed to forget.

But I didn't understand, and I couldn't forgive him. Like the doctors, he had betrayed me.

Coffee and You

The room was filled with unnecessary accessories. There were too many intimate details. I looked around, trying to find a place, a space, a space that would include me – the possibility of an us. I searched everywhere, but even the walls were packed. As I scanned the room, preoccupied with my panic, with my hesitation, we finally locked eyes. Your gaze told me otherwise. The silent desire in your eyes confirmed there was a deeper place for me. *It was with you.* Have you ever been embraced by someone's eyes? It is an uneasy feeling. I wondered if I was making it all up. And then you said "Come back." The air between us vibrates. The walls listen closely. You and I both want to say so much, and yet the silence remains louder than words. It takes everything in me not to tell you what I really want to say. I look at your magnetic eyes, and I am nearly certain they don't sparkle like that for anyone. I wish for a mirror, if only to show you the way you look at me.

As we grow up, we get caught up in our lives, in running after materialism, in work, in establishing ourselves. We start worrying about so many unnecessary things. We forget what it's like to just be genuine. We forget that vulnerability is beautiful, that intimacy is built on shared pain, exposure, and that it really is the small things in life that count. As I look around me, I find that the distance between even the closest couples is immeasurable. There is always a lack of communication, running after approval from each other, or finding flaws in one another. Sometimes, people stay in relationships out of a fear of being alone. Sometimes, they want the protection and the security that comes with it – again, this adult life forgets the small things.

But then you touched my soul and I wish you knew that I am difficult to reach. Those that know me will vouch for this. I'm nearly sure the distance between us must continue to exist. There is an obstacle, as there always is with the good things. But darling, you are far greater than a good thing. Our unspoken dialogue resembled something unrealistic – but we both knew that there was still going to be a promise. You listened, and I wanted to hear you speak more. Your voice pulled me closer, rang in my ears, and left me craving more. And now you have left me going around in circles, mad, thirsty for you, and wondering what could have been. It was a chance encounter, and a separation that was by choice. Logic decided to step in. All is fair in love and war. *But what do I do with the possibility of you haunting me?* I could have built you a home, and you would have poured my morning coffee, as I pour into you.

Wherever you are, I'll still have the coffee you sent my way. You made sure you left your imprint – I wonder if you know that it was never about the coffee. And you were my almost. We almost made it.

Hajir[3]

Farida was in an abusive marriage. She knew it. There was no denying that she was unhappy. She was losing herself, slowly, she could barely recognize herself in the mirror. She looked at her pictures in high school, and she searched for the girl that she used to be. She had dyed her hair blonde years ago, and she had also stopped going to the salon. The black roots were clear as day, and yet, she couldn't bring herself to ask Ali if she could go to the salon. He couldn't trust her, he said, and she didn't have the energy to fight him. So she let her hair grow, her roots contrasting greatly with the blonde hair around her shoulders, and she stopped looking at the mirror, hoping she would disappear from everywhere.

Her bank account was suffering. Ali had access to all of her money, her inheritance, and her salary. She was a teacher, and as much as she wanted to believe that she was a strong woman; she was a fearful and battered woman. It was a secret she could never tell. Ali had been her choice, after all. She had fought her family for

---

[3]   To depart, to leave, to break all ties.

him. She had chosen to marry him, despite her family's disapproval. He was Bidoon[4] and she belonged to a rich, upper-class Kuwaiti family. Because of his social status, he had not completed his high school education. And although they had an ocean of differences between them, she had found herself endlessly gravitating towards him. He was inspiring in his ideals, in his desire to reform the world, in his political ideologies, his desire to resist tyranny, to fight against oppression. He was involved in numerous political parties, and he was always helping those who were less privileged. He was brave and, very, very hungry. He was hungry for justice. For a world that would tip the scales. A world that would grant him status. A world that would cease to insult humanity. Ali's passion was endless. And in the same way, his love for Farida was engulfing, suffocating, and eventually unbearable.

She missed the way she used to go shopping. She missed being able to buy designer bags. He would calculate every dinar spent and ask her to explain her logic behind buying things. She could no longer say "I liked it, and I wanted to buy it." She simply stuttered under his fierce gaze. When he started calling her "stupid" she felt the insult hurl at her as though her soul was being raped. Farida went from being "It Girl" like her friends used to call her, to plain "Stupid." The dark circles under her eyes had defined her unhappiness. Slowly, Farida and Ali stopped talking. They lived in the same house, shared the same bed, and the silence was the only entity uniting them. He stopped reaching out for her, except those nights when he needed to satisfy his own urges, and she stopped responding.

---

4   Of no legal status in Kuwait, a group of people with no citizenship residing in Kuwait.

               Notes on the Flesh

When she said no, insults were thrown her way, and in the morning, the silent treatment ensued.

And that was when she found Jarrah, her old, high school sweetheart. There he was on Facebook, within reach. Just a message away. Just a "Friend Request" away. Jarrah, the boyfriend who nearly married her. The boy who made one mistake – the boy who feared commitment. Jarrah wouldn't marry Farida at the age of twenty-five, and she was getting frustrated with his indecisiveness. She left him, and a month later, met Ali. Ali and Jarrah were opposites. Ali jumped into a relationship with her, demanded to be loved back, and would not take no for an answer. He made her feel desired and worthy. She married him, and never looked back. She cut off all ties with her family, walking out on everyone except Ali. He was her choice.

Three years later, here she is, yearning for Jarrah. Was it fair? Had it been fair to give up on Jarrah? He had asked her to wait for him. In the haste of youth, in the passion and impulsivity of desire, she had broken up with him. They had shared an apartment together when they were studying in the States. Their small apartment suddenly felt surreal. She remembered the way she cooked eggs in the morning, dancing around the kitchen, singing at the top of her lungs, hoping he would wake up before she had to go to class. Her parents didn't know she was living with him, and they were hoping to get away with it. They were studying in Oregon, where there were hardly any Kuwaitis or Arabs. Nobody could talk, nobody could gossip about them. It was a safe haven, until one day, her mother's pressure was too much for Farida to handle.

"You have to find a husband. You're twenty-five, and you can't keep studying. You can't keep running away from home," her mother nagged.

"I'm not running away. I don't need to be married before a certain age!"

The argument was pointless, but her mother had planted the seed in her head. Farida fought with Jarrah, and he attacked her for pressuring him into marriage, nothing but a social contract, a way to make ends meet, a way to cage their love, a way to please society.

"I need this Jarrah," Farida insisted.

"And I need you to let go of your desire to please the world. Just be happy in the moment. Why are you always worried about the end result?" Jarrah questioned her.

They never saw eye to eye. Farida left him with a long explanation that she was not the type of woman who waits for a man to be ready for her.

"You're either in or you're out," she had said.

"I'm out," he replied angrily. She was threatening him, and he wouldn't fall for it. Farida always got her way and he wasn't about to give in.

As she replayed the events in her head, she started looking for a suitcase. She grabbed her things, one by one. Her favorite green scarf. Her makeup. Her laptop. Her Chanel dress. Her work clothes. She tossed everything she could see in front of her into the huge red suitcase.

She called Ali to tell him that she was leaving him.

"What? You crazy woman! Just stay the night and we will talk! You can't leave me! What nonsense is this!" he screamed.

"I'm not crazy. I have had enough," she replied calmly.

Her calmness and her cold tone immediately sent Ali into a frenzy of begging, promises to change, spluttering forgiveness requests, and loving eulogies.

"Just one more chance. Please. Stay for tonight and then if you still want to leave me tomorrow you can," he concluded. He was out of breath, and felt he was about to lose her for good.

She sighed. She couldn't bear to see him in so much pain. She felt cruel and unfeeling, and this was not how she wanted him to remember her. They had shared good memories. There was a love between them, even though he had killed it. It was her that he had murdered, ever so gracefully, ever so subtly.

"I'll stay the night Ali. Relax," she responded monotonously.

"Thank you, thank you! I'll be back in an hour, let me just finish up here," Ali said, completely relieved.

At seven PM that night, he walked into their apartment and headed straight to the bedroom. The first thought he had was to open the closet. Nothing. Empty. The dresses were gone. The shoes were gone. He panicked. He rushed to the bathroom, looking for her toothbrush, her night cream. Not a trace of her was left. It was as though he had been living alone all along.

He started circling the living room. Looking for a sign, anything. And there it was. She had left him a note on the coffee table. She knew him too well, she had known that he was bound to throw himself on the couch and stare into space. The white A4 paper stared at him. He unfolded the paper, his fingers trembling. There was her handwriting that he loved so much, screaming at him:

I am sorry. I have to leave you. You'll never forgive me. Farida.

And with the howl of a madman, he threw his head back and groaned wildly, rejected from the world, from his love. She was gone. Nothing but an echo. For seventy nights, he slept on the couch, left with no explanations, no closures, and no attempt at reconciliation.

Forty

They say that's how long as it takes to grieve. Forty nights. I spent the days in bed, listening to every verse of the Quran I could think of. Then, at night, I listened to Metallica. I was angry, I was desperate, and I was overcome with a longing that I had never known before. Every night at three AM, I woke up to the sound of the *athan*. [5] The sound of prayer urged me to get up, to roam around the house. The empty house mocked me. The chairs had been left undusted, untouched. I hadn't changed the bedsheets, hoping to still be able to catch your scent. Everyone warned me that I wasn't grieving properly. I wasn't doing it right. I wasn't following the Stages of Grief. I was refusing to move on.

How do you move on when the biggest part of you is seized by Azrael[6]? He had taken you straight from my arms, that night, when all I wanted was to hold on tight. Your brown hair fell across your forehead, damp, sweaty, your face covered in tears.

"Don't let me go," you whispered.

---

[5]   Muslim Prayer

[6]   Angel of death.

I remember thinking I was God. I remember thinking that if I believed I wouldn't lose you, I would win this war. I didn't know I was that incompetent. In the face of death, I was humbled.

You didn't want to leave me to the memories. You knew your time was almost up. How we feared time. Together, we thought we could always live in the moment. Never worry about tomorrow. But the truth of the matter was, we were always cautious, fully aware that the shadow of time was looming closer, always haunting us, always threatening to take you away.

We had spoken about my life after you. You had urged me to fall in love again, to re-marry. To find a home, to find peace, to find a woman who would take care of me.

"I can't," I said to the mirror. Confession: I still see your face in the mirror. I still see the way you used to paint your lips red for me, and the way your eyelashes took forever to curl. I look at the mirror and I am afraid to blink. Blinking takes me away from you. If I turn my face, you're gone again.

They told me that what I was doing was eventually going to hurt me. You didn't have a chance at life, but why would I do the same to myself? This wasn't love. Love was supposed to be healthy and good for you. I was constantly choking on memories of us. I was drowning in remnants of you, of your voice, of the scent of your perfume, and the way you insisted that I take my vitamins every morning.

The complexity of life and death. The way we are always stuck on a boat, floating aimlessly. The boat simply floats. It doesn't know when, and if, it will sink. It simply knows it doesn't stand a chance amidst the storm. I wondered if I would ever forget the boat that

Notes on the Flesh

took you from me. Grief takes time. And yet again, time takes even more time. The equation was never going to be understood. I was never going to find my answers. I spoke to angels. I spoke to psychics. I spoke to Allah, at dawn. I prayed for life to be kinder, I prayed for you to be in heaven, and I wanted to see where you were. Was heaven accessible? Could I find you there? I was at a loss, and there was no home left for me. What else could I do, except pray for you to visit me in my dreams? *Everyone around me thought I was going mad, I was losing faith in Allah's wisdom, but I was certain you didn't want me to give up on you.*

Epilogue

Loss is still a very daunting entity, fear-inspiring and I am always worried about the future. When you know that there is impending doom, that you will lose a part of yourself to a disease that completely takes over, one cannot help but fear the future. We are all aware that the future is elusive, but I think chronically ill individuals and people with disabilities are more aware of the looming future, the shadow of loss, the rape of the body, the destruction of the senses, and the negotiation of a new sense of self. Is myself just my body? Must it be a body that is lovable? A body that is healed only through love? Whose love? Should it be mine? Is self-love the answer? But we need human connection, human touch. We need to be acknowledged, approved as worthy of love, deemed human, stamped as "good". To break away from boundaries, borders of the mind, the taboo of the body, what is it that we need? Is it just desire? And, is desire for the terminally ill romantic? Is desire a part of life, a love for life? What do you do when society claims to know your body better, when it insists on cleansing the spirit, making you better, a purer version of you? So many turn to religion for comfort, for salvation. Others turn to drugs. Others turn to music. Some turn to writing. Some become eternally numbed, afraid of human connection. In a society that continues to separate, harmony becomes a dream, a dream that is not only deferred until further notice, but at many times seems like a delusion.

It has been over a decade of experiments, and perhaps this is life. Just an experiment, variables changing, and outcomes that are, in the end, ultimately unexpected. There is a randomness that I have to accept. Just like this book's randomness. If it has provided anything at all, then maybe my existence in this body is not random after all. Throughout the different voices, these lovers are in the end, lovers of love, lovers of life, lovers of lovers, and are as accidentally victims of society's unlove of love.

About the Author

Shahd Alshammari holds a PhD in English from the University of Kent in England. She currently teaches literature and women's studies in Kuwait.

Her main research areas are Disability and Women's studies. Her work sheds light on the struggles facing those conflicted over cultural traditions, societal norms and modernity. She has published in academic and creative writing journals such as Journal of Literary and Cultural Disability Studies, Journal of Middle East Women's Studies, Pomona Valley Review and The Barefoot Review. This is Dr Alshammari's first collection of short stories.

47994691R00070

Made in the USA
San Bernardino, CA
14 April 2017